Praise for

People First

"Amy Lafko's engaging approach to storytelling provides a roadmap for reinvigorating your teams and your career... putting people first!"

ALAN AYERS, president, Experity; Lifetime Membership Award, Urgent Care Association; senior editor, *Journal of Urgent Care Medicine*

"Each chapter of *People First* will force you to see things from an entirely different perspective. Amy Lafko is a guide along the path of the People First method."

CRAIG KNACK, CPC, CMPE, director, Practice Operations Cardiology, Vascular, Urology, Patient Experience, St. Peter's Health Partners

"*People First* makes it clear why focusing on your people is the first step to business success. Amy Lafko's simple, actionable approach to the complex world of personnel management will give any owner or leader needing direction a clear path forward."

DEREK FENWICK, PT, MBA, SHRM-SCP, senior director, human resources, Infinity Rehab; nominating committee, American Physical Therapy Association

"Amy Lafko's vulnerability in sharing lessons she learned the hard way sparked a new level of clarity and energy for my own leadership path."

HEATHER JENNINGS, PT, DPT, director, American Physical Therapy Association

"This is a wonderful model! I learned that clearly stating and defining goals and giving team members the 'bigger picture' at the start of each meeting helps them be more engaged and helps focus the conversation and actions. It also creates purpose and motivation to continue a certain action toward a goal."
SARAH GERRISH, MD, faculty, Family Medicine Residency of Idaho–Boise and chair, Justice, Equity, Diversity, and Inclusion; instructor, University of Washington School of Medicine

"I believe when leaders take good care of their people, the people will, in turn, take good care of their customers. In the healthcare industry, where the patient is the customer, Amy Lafko's principles of leadership follow suit: when leaders in healthcare focus on caring for their people first, everyone feels better about their job and the patient/customer is the ultimate winner. Read *People First* and learn how putting your people first is the best way to serve your patients."
KEN BLANCHARD, coauthor of *The New One Minute Manager®* and *Servant Leadership in Action*

"People First is a leadership discipline that every medical leader should adopt and exercise. Amy Lafko has formed a schematic of guiding-truth principles that she has practiced over the course of her medical career. Her honesty and openness provide sage wisdom that leaders can pull confidence from to grow their team, as well as their business."
MATTHEW OLMES, general dentist, Susquehanna Valley Dental Health Associates

"Building and running a fantastic healthcare practice is essential (for society) and exhausting (for you). You'll find strategies for sustainable, people-centered growth in this practical book that will help you work less hard while increasing your impact and reach."

MICHAEL BUNGAY STANIER, author of *The Coaching Habit*

"*People First* provides a practical approach to assessment, design, and delivery methods for building or growing a successful organization. Amy Lafko shares her professional journey with refreshing candor and humility; her stories of learning from failure will resonate with emerging and seasoned leaders. Transforming her passion into action, Amy has gained recognition as a leader in guiding organizations to greater success by focusing on their most valuable resource— their people."

PATTY MCGUIRE, vice president, operations, WellSpan Health

"Excellent, well-researched, evidence-based content. A must-have for healthcare leaders of today's organizations."

ROGER CONNORS, 4x *New York Times*– and *Wall Street Journal*–bestselling author and coauthor of the No. 1 bestselling book, *Get A Coach | Be A Coach*

"*People First* inspires the mindset needed to finally reboot healthcare. It is the instruction manual and the toolkit all in one."

STACEY ZEIGLER, PT, associate editor, *Learning to Lead in Physical Therapy*; founder/owner, Fun in Aging Physical Therapy

"By embracing the People First mentality, Amy Lafko shows us that by prioritizing our team we are able to better serve and connect with our community. This book is an amazing guide and reminder for all business owners and leaders."

TERRI MAZAHERI, owner and founder, Inside Out Aesthetics

"Leading a successful healthcare practice has become a lot easier. Each page of Amy Lafko's book, *People First*, bursts with practical and powerful ideas that will immediately help you think and lead differently. Simply a great no-nonsense field guide to improve all aspects of your healthcare business."

DR. VINCE MOLINARO, strategic leadership advisor, keynote speaker, and *New York Times*–bestselling author of *The Leadership Contract*

"*People First* lays out the steps to make the fourth leg of the quadruple aim, our people, the rock on which we build our futures. Countless times I have been in boardrooms wrestling the patient first, people first question. With a room full of direct patient care owner physicians, patient first nearly always won the argument. How could we have framed the conversation differently, particularly with physician owners, so all patients would be better served by coming in second to the people in our care? This book prepares you for that discussion and for the evolution/revolution in your practice."

KAREN S. SIMONTON, CPA, strategic alliance director, The OrthoForum

PEOPLE FIRST

A Proven Method for an
Exceptional Healthcare Practice

AMY LAFKO

*Stay on the
People First Path.*

Amy Lafko

PAGE TWO

Cataloguing in publication information is available from
Library and Archives Canada.
ISBN 978-1-77458-120-9 (paperback)
ISBN 978-1-77458-121-6 (ebook)

Page Two
pagetwo.com

Edited by Brooke White
Copyedited by Steph VanderMeulen
Proofread by Alison Strobel
Cover, interior design, and illustrations by Jennifer Lum

thepeoplefirstbook.com

CONTENTS

Introduction: Meet You on Your Path   1

1   The People First Path   9

Part One: THINK

2   The Foundational Rock of Organizational Design   27

3   The THINK Leadership Factor   45

Part Two: SAY

4   The Weight of Words   63

5   Systems for Communication and Connection   75

6   The SAY Leadership Factor   91

Part Three: DO

7   Align and Inspire: The People First Approach to Onboarding and Orientation   107

8   Engage and Empower: The People First Approach to Retention   121

9   Attract and Select: The People First Approach to Recruiting and Hiring   141

10   The DO Leadership Factor   157

Part Four: GROW

11 Plan, Execute, and Learn   173

12 Change Is the Only Constant   189

13 The 7 Stages of Growth   203

14 The GROW Leadership Factor   217

Part Five: THE PATH CONTINUES

15 Are We There Yet?   235

Acknowledgments   243

Notes   245

For my Mom—my foundational rock

Introduction:
Meet You on Your Path

I F YOU ARE the owner, leader, or administrator of a healthcare practice and you're looking for a path to lasting and rewarding growth, you've come to the right place. This book invites you to explore a proven and straightforward method to design your organization with intention and purpose, to improve your leadership skills, and to get curious about ways to grow your people so you can grow your business.

The People First path is designed using your organization's unique value proposition along with a set of best-practice intentions, language, and behaviors. It will allow you to up-level your practice by creating an overall experience of team engagement resulting in decreased confusion, overwhelm, and many of the other challenges that accidentally creep into the healthcare work environment, including:

- Too much time spent putting out fires or dealing with crises and chaos

- Feelings of being stretched too thin or nearing burnout

- Good but not best-in-class patient satisfaction

- Stalled patient volumes

- Smaller than desired profit margins

- Productivity below industry averages

- Higher than acceptable staff turnover

- People not doing what they are supposed to do

- Staff often saying, "I don't know"

- Superficial trust within the leadership team

- Resistance to making changes to move the practice forward

If any of these challenges resonate with you, don't despair! There is a way out of these dark woods, and wherever you are on your path, I'm honored to meet you there.

Perhaps you're in the process of mapping out your private practice and trying to decide what you want the overall experience to be. You're filled with energy and ready to put some miles on your shoes. You'll save yourself a lot of headaches and wrong turns with this guide to organizational design, and the path is yours to carve.

Perhaps you're already well on your way to running a successful practice and you want a change of scenery. Are you working harder than necessary to stay on track? Maybe you've reached a summit and can't see your way to the next one? This book will guide you through the peaks and valleys of redesigning your operation for the optimal view.

Or perhaps you're deep in the woods, bushwhacking to find your way back to the trail. Are you experiencing turmoil within your culture or time-sucking turnover? Is your staff taking their job dissatisfaction and frustration out on patients? Is there a lack of accountability in your organization?

By reading this book, you are on the path to growing your business through increased staff and patient satisfaction, improved productivity, and enhanced efficiency. Equally important, you won't be putting out fires all the time or stretching yourself too thin because you've taken on too much.

Cairns: A Visual Navigational Tool

Growing up on the East Coast, hiking in the woods was fairly straightforward. The dirt and leaves on the trail were beaten down by other hikers, which made the path clearly visible. When I moved to the high desert of Grand Junction, Colorado, hiking trails were trickier to navigate. The orange-red slick rock prevented a clear path from emerging, and sometimes the path was impossible to discern. It was not uncommon for me to hike along thinking I was heading in the right direction only to discover I was off course.

It was out there, in vast Mesa County, that I discovered the importance of cairns: beautifully balanced rock formations that are universally known to hikers as a signal that they are on the right track.[1] I love how cairns look, what they symbolize, and, most importantly, their value as a navigational tool.

Picture this: You're out hiking with a map you studied carefully before you hit the trail. The route seemed clear before you started, but now, you're not sure if you're going the right way. Maybe you've come to a place where the path divides, and you've got a choice to make. You look at the map again and confusion sets in. Suddenly, you're not at all sure which way to go.

Assessing the trail division, you notice a pile of rocks positioned next to a particular path, and you're flooded with relief. This isn't an ordinary pile of rocks. It's a cairn built by people who have gone before you: people who have gotten where you want to go. Reflecting the unique perspective of whoever built them, cairns serve one of three main purposes:

1. To establish the best path forward by providing a trail marker

2. To clarify the better route when a path diverges

3. To draw attention to obstacles or pitfalls that are hidden from view

The simplicity and practicality of cairns struck me so deeply, I named my business Cairn Consulting Solutions. With more than twenty years of leadership experience in the healthcare field, I appreciate how critical the right guiding structure is to a practice leader's success—just as important as it is out on the trail.

Owning or leading a healthcare practice sometimes feels like being lost in the woods, and I know how scary it is to be unsure of which direction to take. I've been there. In fact, the reason I wrote this book is that I've taken the wrong path on my own leadership journey more times than I care to admit. With the benefit of hindsight and armed with hard lessons learned along the way, I want to save you from taking the same wrong turns I did.

The Power of People before Patients

Many practice owners and leaders are guided by the outdated, yet still indoctrinated, "patient first" mindset. On the surface, this makes sense because, of course, patients are the business we are in, and we want them to have a positive outcome. We want them to come back and to refer their friends. That said, unless you are a one-person organization, you rely on *other* people to help you achieve patient satisfaction.

The reality is, the "patient first" mindset is a relic of the past. It's a leftover from an outdated framework initiated by the Institute for Healthcare Improvement (IHI) known as the Triple Aim, which focuses on:

1. Improving the experience of care

2. Improving the health of populations

3. Reducing per capita costs of healthcare[2]

The healthcare industry has largely adopted this framework. However, it does not take into consideration our healthcare clinicians' stressful work lives or how that stress impacts their ability to care for patients. This, to me, is the crux of the dilemma that practice owners and leaders face today. The system is designed for patients while it ignores the very people who are expected to care for them.

> The system is designed for patients while it ignores the very people who are expected to care for them.

As a leader, I've struggled with the challenges associated with care, health, and costs. Eventually, I discovered my own personal guiding philosophy, or my own cairn, if you will: "Grow your people to grow your business." And how does one grow their people to grow their business? By putting their people first!

Without prioritizing the needs of the people who deliver healthcare services, it's unrealistic to expect that patients will have the best experience every time. When owners, administrators, medical assistants, physicians, and clinicians are exhausted, how can they muster the energy to go beyond providing a safe visit to creating an exceptional experience? What about delivering innovative care in a practice that has optimized efficiency and effectiveness? Or a practice that can sustain any challenge, grow when the timing is right, and be regarded as the best in the community? Or, dare to dream, a practice where team members stay for years because they love it, and you—the owner—are still energized by the work?

I've seen firsthand the superior effectiveness of a People First approach to organizational design. Through a collaborative process, I've made a career out of helping healthcare practices shift from the patient first mentality to People First. This book harnesses those experiences and builds the business case for you and your organization to make the shift too.

Build Your Own Cairn:
How to Get the Most Out of This Book

Within these pages, you'll learn how to build a cairn that will guide you toward both organizational and leadership success on the People First path. This success comes through understanding your practice's unique value proposition, and then learning the mindset and skill set of growing your people to grow your business.

A cairn is made up of layers of rocks: each one solid and large enough to support the others. Building a cairn that stands tall enough to be a guide requires balancing the rocks in a way that prevents a collapse. Likewise, designing a People First healthcare practice requires solid and well-balanced principles and actions. Within this model, the four rocks for organizational design and personal leadership are THINK, SAY, DO, and GROW.

THINK is the foundational rock of People First because it encompasses your mindset, your beliefs, and your intentions. Every action you take and every word you say is based on how you THINK. If your mindset and intentions don't truly support "people before patients," then what you SAY and DO and how you GROW won't lead to long-term success.

If you don't believe that your people should come before patients, I'm afraid you won't find much to build on here. If, however, you are open to exploring this mindset, you can experiment with your own organizational rocks. (Trust me, there is much opportunity ahead when you begin with the right mindset and intentions.)

This book is organized into four parts to represent the four rocks in the People First structural cairn: THINK, SAY, DO, and GROW, plus a final part on continuing your path. Each part begins with a concentration on organizational design considerations. I've dedicated the majority of the book to organizational design because even outstanding leaders struggle against an organizational design that doesn't support People First.

You will find experiments, called "Self-Checks," at the end of each organizational design chapter. The Self-Checks are intended to help you dig into the specifics of your practice, and analyze what could or should be changed to be more aligned with a People First mindset.

Each part concludes with a focus on the leadership skills related to the THINK, SAY, DO, and GROW rocks of your cairn. Your cairn won't stand the test of time without skilled leaders grounded in the People First mindset. With hundreds of books on leadership already available, I've selected key elements of success that are often overlooked. While you will also find "Self-Checks" here, use each whole chapter as an opportunity to decide where you excel and where you struggle, then start to experiment.

Through personal experiences, case studies, interviews with practice owners and leaders, and immediately applicable Self-Checks, you'll learn how to build and balance a cairn that is uniquely yours. You'll also learn what obstacles to avoid and discover better routes to take as you grow your business and develop your leadership skill set.

To get the most out of this book, I recommend you read it in its entirety, front to back, as presented. This approach will allow you to take in the whole bird's-eye view of the People First path before doubling back to revisit your focus areas.

At times, the path to success can be hard to see. There are a lot of weeds, fallen branches, and overgrowth blocking the view. It's important that your cairn is tall enough and strong enough to be seen, especially when you feel lost. Building a cairn is a creative process of discovery, exploration, and curiosity. While the methods have been proved, you'll need to explore how to make them authentic to you and your practice. You will need to experiment to find the correct balance for your practice.

Now, let's get started. Your path is calling. I'll meet you there.

1

The People First Path

WELCOME TO THE People First path, a proven method for healthcare practice owners and leaders to fully engage their teams by putting people before patients. It is the culmination of extensive research, lessons learned the hard way, and best practices from incredible leaders and organizations.

We will explore the "who, what, when, where, and how" of the People First approach in depth but we begin with why it matters. In 2009, Simon Sinek published his first bestselling book, *Start with Why*. It was a smash hit in leadership circles. In it, he says if you want to inspire people and motivate them to take action, they need to understand *why* it matters for them. The "why" is fundamental: so let's look at why the People First path matters for *you*.

Why You Should Care:
The Business Case for People First

In healthcare, we rely on data for proof, so I'll begin with a few data points that confirm *why* the employee experience matters.

- A 2016 study by Susan Collier and colleagues demonstrated a strong positive relationship between total engagement score and total patient safety score (r = 0.645, P < .01) and positive relationships between total engagement score and the twelve safety culture dimensions.[1]

- Analysis of Press Ganey data reveals that better employee engagement correlates with better outcomes in safety and technical quality.[2]

- Highly engaged teams are 21% more productive.[3]

- Employee engagement results in a 41% reduction in absenteeism.[4]

Beyond the data, proof also comes through trial and error. In 2007, the Institute for Healthcare Improvement (IHI) created the Triple Aim as "a framework for optimizing health system performance by simultaneously focusing on the health of a population, the experience of care for individuals within that population, and the per capita cost of providing that care."[5] Notice that improving the patient experience of care is the priority, and IHI stresses that the Triple Aim is about patients. The Triple Aim became widely accepted in all areas of healthcare, and yet, this model left a void in achieving that positive patient experience—the people providing the care.

In 2014, an article in the *Annals of Family Medicine,* written by medical doctors Thomas Bodenheimer and Christine Sinsky, shared the results of a study of primary care practices, titled "From Triple to Quadruple Aim: Care of the Patient Requires Care of the Provider." The article gets to the root of the problem with a patient first model. It states: "We have adopted the Triple Aim as our framework, but the stressful work life of our clinicians and staff impacts our ability to achieve the 3 aims."[6]

While the Quadruple Aim is acknowledged, few practices have made the shift to carry out that fourth aim: bringing joy to the workplace, preventing burnout among healthcare providers, and creating of a sense of personal accomplishment. Practices that truly adjust their aim to People First exceed the goals of the triple aim *plus* prevent burnout.

Throughout this book, you'll read many stories that prove People First works. It provides the foundation that will allow your practice and patients to thrive and grow, by helping your *people* thrive and grow.

Who Are Your People?

The "people" in People First are every single member of your team: from the frontline staff to the clinicians, the medical assistants, the managers, the administrators, the leaders, and the owners. Yes, *you*, the leader and/or owner, are part of People First too.

Consider the patient's journey in your organization. Who is their first point of contact? What interactions shape their visit? The people who interact immediately and directly with the patient are the front office staff, then clinicians or a physician, then perhaps the billing person or the scheduler.

Let's face it: you probably interact with the people on your team way more than you interact with the majority of your patients. Depending on the size of your practice, there could be two or more people between you and the patient. As the organization grows, the size of the hierarchy grows too.

> You can't go
> around your
> own people
> to create
> the patient
> experience.

You can't go around your own people to create the patient experience. You can try but it won't have the best patient outcome, you'll be exhausted, and the staff will leave in frustration. Instead, focus on creating a positive experience for your people, so they can create a positive experience for the patient.

You'll notice the sample organizational charts (shown below) are horizontal instead of vertical. While traditional organizational charts represent a top-down hierarchy, I've purposely flipped the concept on its side. People First is not about who is on top of the chart or queen of the mountain; it's about working side-by-side with your team until those people get all the way to the patient. Take a look.

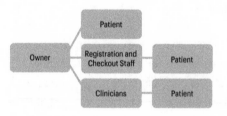

Whatever your level is within the organization, you support and serve the people *next to you* on the organizational chart, not the people two or three steps away. Even if there is only one person between you and the patient, you must focus on that one person. How many people are between you and the patient your organization serves?

Many years ago, when I was a clinical leader, I used to think, "Being a clinical leader is great because I get to impact more patients every day than I would if I were treating patients myself." My rationale was that if I treated fourteen patients a day, I impacted fourteen lives, and if I had ten employees who treated fourteen patients a day, I impacted 140 patients. I was the very definition of a multiplier, or so I thought.

In reality, by looking only at the final number (140 patients) and skipping over the ten people next to me, I wasn't multiplying great clinical care. I was burning out clinicians and frustrating them to the point at which they either left or couldn't give their best to every patient every time. It wasn't until I shifted to the People First path that I realized I wasn't a true multiplier unless I put my energy into my own people, so *they could become the multipliers.*

What Is People First?

People First is a method of designing your healthcare practice combined with a philosophy of leadership. Intentional organizational design plus intentional leadership geared toward putting people's needs first creates an environment in which employees can be their best—inspired and motivated to go above and beyond for the organization and the people it serves. People First allows for an experience of engagement instead of an experience of confusion, low trust, and lack of commitment.

When explaining best practices for organizational design, I use one of my favorite metaphors—a rock cairn—to illustrate People First business solutions for healthcare practices. As I mentioned in the Introduction, a cairn is a human-made pile of stones, most often found on hiking trails, that indicate in which direction to continue. On the People First path, the cairn is made up of four rocks: THINK, SAY, DO, and GROW.

> People First allows for an experience of engagement.

You cannot build a cairn with a single rock, which is why the foundational rock of People First design, THINK, is so critical. It represents an organization's mindset and intentions, which is the basis upon which all other functions of the business rest. If an organization's THINK is not strong or sturdy enough, it cannot support SAY and DO, and you won't be able to build a lasting cairn to guide you as you GROW.

SAY is the language an organization uses and its system of communication. Words have a way of impacting behaviors, and for this reason, SAY supports the DO rock. DO is the organization's processes, systems, and activities plus the leader's behaviors. You'll find situations in which SAY comes before DO and vice versa. This flexibility is one of the many benefits of constructing your own cairn based on your organization's unique intentions, mindset, and vision. Just remember, THINK is always the foundation.

THINK, SAY, and DO are required to build a cairn that is tall and sturdy enough to guide you when the path forward isn't clear. The fourth rock, GROW, is the pinnacle that allows you to see even further ahead and move quickly in the direction you want to go. Growth means more than expanding revenue, patient volume, or the number of clinics under your umbrella. Growth takes many forms, but at its core, it is an integral part of not just surviving, but thriving.

An organization that supports and celebrates People First looks something like the diagram here:

In the chapters ahead, we'll explore each of the rocks in the People First cairn, by examining trends, statistics, and stories from those who have carved the path before you. I'll share tools and experimental Self-Checks to help you design a practice that supports its people while also experiencing the benefits of:

- Clarity on individual and organizational goals and priorities

- Enhanced management and staff communication and trust

- A thorough accountability system

- A strategic approach to growth

With such structures in place, business owners and leaders can, at minimum, look forward to the following results:

- Leadership team alignment

- Dwindling symptoms of burnout and fatigue

- A lower rate of employee turnover

- Improved critical thinking and decision making

- Increased patient satisfaction

If these results sound appealing to you, and you're willing to experiment, you are ripe for organizational change.

What People First Is Not

Just as important as understanding why People First matters—what exactly it is and who your people are—is understanding what People First is not. Contrary to what many people assume, People First is not a method that ignores business imperatives or financial realities.

Mike Michalowicz, author of *Profit First*, says you absolutely must understand your numbers or you won't have a business for long.[7] I agree with him, and I'd like to draw attention to the fact that there is a difference between knowing your numbers and putting finances before your people.

People First is not an either-or situation. You don't need to choose between finances, patients, business initiatives, or your people. Instead, it's a way of viewing your role as a leader and owner who consistently keeps people at the center, in both good times and bad, and in tandem with your overall organizational goals.

Not too long ago, I was talking to a client who was struggling to keep his business afloat during the COVID-19 lockdown. He called to talk about the reality of having to lay people off amid the roller coaster of uncertainty about when he might be able to reopen. There was a $200,000 implication to keeping everyone employed. For the business to survive, he had to make some hard decisions. Yet, he had a People First mindset and truly cared about them all. His angst was real.

He met with each team member individually to explain the situation and articulate his concern for everyone on a personal level. He asked for their thoughts and told them about his plan to bring them back as soon as possible. After the layoffs, he stayed connected to make sure they were doing OK and to update them on how things looked from his end.

Since that dark time, I'm happy to report, he was able to resume full-time operations and rehire his whole staff. The team came back with their heads and hearts fully engaged. They knew how much he cared about them and worked harder than ever to help the organization grow for the future.

My client was able to save his team (and his business) by showing his people they mattered. He understood his numbers—as Mike Michalowicz emphasized—but he also put his people first. As soon as he was able to bring his whole team back, they helped him get up and running again, his patients received excellent care, and the business was able to survive with renewed vigor. My client's experience proves that putting people first does not ignore business imperatives: it fuels them.

Where People First Came From: My Personal Shift

My path to becoming a People First leader started out strong, but I definitely took a few wrong turns along the way. I'm not afraid to share the good, the bad, and the ugly. We're all on a learning journey, and mine had a few painful moments that, in time, became lessons.

A Strong Start Is Critical

At the beginning of my career, I was proud to be a clinician at one of the best trauma hospitals in the country, the R Adams Cowley Shock Trauma Center in Baltimore. I loved working with the patients in the ICU. While working there, I was the proud recipient of the Hero Award: a badge of honor that meant the world to me.

Then, my path took an unexpected turn. I was all of twenty-seven years old when I became the director of Rehab at another facility. I have to tell you, the next four years were a blast. I was part of growing a department in which incredibly skilled clinicians thrived. Every once in a while, I helped a therapist with a treatment plan in my realm of expertise, but for the most part, I just let them do their thing. They were great therapists, but more importantly, they were engaged in patient care and sincerely wanted to make the organization a better place. We started programs that were the first of their kind, not only at that facility but in the state.

As much as I cared about our patients, I wasn't focused on them. I simply wanted the people I worked with to enjoy their work so they could do their best. Because I was focused on my team and what they were able to achieve, I can confidently say that our patients received exceptional care.

Interestingly, and inherently, I was a People First leader without even realizing it.

Part of the reason I wanted to be a great leader was that I *had* great leaders. The president and vice president of the organization were incredibly supportive. Rarely did they ask about a particular patient's care or a specific therapist's treatment plan. They modeled People First leadership by asking what I needed to be successful, which meant I could focus on the therapy team so they could thrive. My bosses got the best of my ideas and inspiration—my highest level of engagement—and the team I supported gave me theirs.

As much as I loved the job and my life in Baltimore, it wasn't all gumdrops and roses. Like every organization, we had to let go of low performers as well as address challenging regulatory and payer changes. Focusing on the people allowed us to weather those storms.

Eventually, I left the job in Maryland to become a contract therapist, which allowed me to work for thirteen-week stints in different locations as well as enjoy time in between contracts for my true passion: travel. I was fortunate enough to tour through Southeast Asia, South America, New Zealand, Antarctica, and beyond. I even found time to become a scuba diving instructor in Hawaii.

After a shoulder dislocation cut one of my contracts short, I decided it was time to get a "real" job. A new position as the director of Rehab in a Level 1 trauma center took me back to my home state of Pennsylvania. I knew what great care looked like from my time in the ICU, and I was excited to get back to Acute Care.

Surviving versus Thriving in Acute Care

The new position did not go well. I want to be clear: I own my role in the failure of that experience and don't blame anyone else. The following account is a recollection of my viewpoint, as it was at the time. I'm sharing it to illustrate how I needed to shift my perspective to become the leader I aspired to be.

When hired, I was told the team I was to oversee was not high-performing. After interacting with them, my perception was that they were lazy and entitled, unwilling to work with challenging patients or to step up to fill holes in the schedule. It seemed to me that this team didn't want to contribute one ounce beyond the bare minimum. Instead of taking the time to learn about their challenges or frustrations, I stuck with my belief that many of them (not all) were denigrating the entire rehab profession. Without empathy or a shred of emotional intelligence for what they might be up against, I basically got really pissed off. And I stayed that way.

It was a toxic environment, and while I wasn't the only problem, my early-career inclinations toward a People First mindset flew right out the window. No one was thriving in that environment: not the team, not the patients, and certainly not me. I was in pure survival mode.

I grew to hate work as much as the team did. It was painful to go in every day, wondering what bad things would happen next. Waiting for the other shoe to drop, I couldn't sleep or concentrate. The anxiety over losing something I never had to begin with—the team's trust and commitment—became unbearable. (I cringe to think of people from that team reading this book. They knew me only when I was a clinician leader who didn't put her people first.) Needless to say, it was a dark time professionally and personally.

Eventually, my boss said, "Amy, we can't keep you in Acute Care anymore. But I'm willing to give you a shot in Home Care." The news was a kick in the gut when I was already down. He punctuated the announcement with a caveat: "Don't screw it up." The "or else" implication was clear. I knew nothing about Home Care. It was the only healthcare setting I'd never worked in.

Home Care Is Where the Heart Is

It turns out, knowing nothing was my most valuable asset. I went into Home Care with a beginner's mindset because that's what I was: a total newbie. I tagged along with the therapists when they went to visit patients, so I could get a glimpse into their world. Right away, I saw how good they were, and I appreciated how they approached their work. I got to know them as people, and through those relationships, I discovered my true leadership role. My job was to support them—to make their work easier and more efficient so they could focus on the patients.

All I could do was learn how to best protect the clinicians in the field. And that's exactly what I did. I got curious and looked to them for answers. My language switched from "Why do you do X, Y, Z?" to "Help me understand what happens if... Help me understand why... Help me understand how..." And they were happy to share the "ifs, whys, and hows" of what they did.

The Home Care clinicians' professionalism and generosity allowed me to experiment and learn, and without being fully conscious of what it meant at the time, I put those therapists first. I put them before the patients and the organization, and even me, because they needed me. And it worked!

The Urgency of Learning to Care

After three formative years in Home Care, I was asked to move over to Urgent Care, which was struggling in every way. My VP thought I might be able to help make some improvements. Still—and forever—humbled by my experience in Acute Care, I went into Urgent Care with the same curious mindset that had worked so well in Home Care.

I quickly discovered that the issues were many: daily patient complaints, high turnover, location closures, providers yelling at patients, and more. The managers were functioning with the same the patient first mindset I'd had in Acute Care. I recognized that the best thing I could do was help the Urgent Care leaders find a different approach and learn how to put their people first.

It dawned on me that if I'd taken a People First approach back when I was in Acute Care, things might have ended on a better note. The people I oversaw in Acute Care were never shown the support or empathy they needed to feel motivated and engaged. Their perceived laziness was the result of feeling uncared for and undervalued. Who can be expected to bring their A game when they feel that way?

There's a strange relief in knowing that if you're part of the problem, you can be part of the solution.

It took some doing and patience, but I was able to help the leadership team in Urgent Care put people first. In many cases, we discovered that the "problem people" weren't actually the problem; leadership was the problem. There's a strange relief in knowing that if you're part of the problem, you can be part of the solution.

In time, we turned the ship around. Employee satisfaction scores went up, the volume of call-outs went down, and we no longer faced the daily threat of having to close a location due to lack of staff. We started to receive patient compliments instead of complaints.

Even if you know your practice inside and out, you can still bring a beginner's mindset to the problems it may be facing. Get curious about the best ways to serve and motivate the team. Ask them, directly, what they need to perform better. I promise, you'll be surprised by what you learn when you stop assuming you know the best way forward.

It wasn't until later in my career that I came up with the language for the People First path, and the rocks within the cairn that support it: THINK, SAY, DO, and GROW. A few years ago, while giving a presentation, I shared my personal guiding philosophy, "Grow your people to grow your business," and people responded immediately. From that mantra, the People First path and the methods to bring it to life were born.

While the path may not always feel clear, stick with it. If you have the right design, it is easier for People First leaders to be successful. The future of work depends on people, and how they are led will determine how they perform.

Self-Check: Where Are You on the People First Path?

Self-awareness is required for growth. Each Self-Check experiment in this book asks for reflection and an assessment of where you are in your journey. If you don't know where you are, you won't know what steps to take or which direction to head in to reach your destination.

Where are you along your own path to becoming a People First organization?

ORGANIZATION

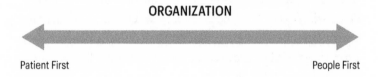

Patient First   People First

How far along the path are you toward People First leadership?

INDIVIDUAL

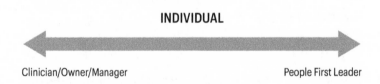

Clinician/Owner/Manager   People First Leader

ONE

THINK

2

The Foundational Rock of Organizational Design

SEAN BAGBEY, Craig Phifer, and Shelly Tyler worked together as therapists for years. Craig says the organization they worked for was "growing quickly just by taking really great care of people." When it was acquired, the new leadership style was not congruent with the leadership style the three colleagues believed in.

During many Wednesday night discussions, they realized they could start their own practice that allowed them to, as Sean says, "live what they believe." They wanted to build a company and a community that changed the way healthcare was delivered.

Craig is forthcoming in saying they didn't have the perfect business plan when they first started out. Really, the only thing they had was "a financial idea of how to put therapists in a good position to succeed with their patients."

Built on the idea of putting their people first, Rehabilitation & Performance Institute (RPI) grew to nine shareholders/owners, twenty-nine employees, and six locations in just four years. The company demonstrated that walking the People First path leads to quick growth, extraordinary patient outcomes, and financial success.

The nonnegotiable foundational rock of the People First cairn is THINK, which is composed of organizational mindset, intentions, and leadership team alignment. While RPI launched their company with People First THINK, you can design and redesign your systems and leadership style at any time. As long as you've got the right mindset and intentions, it's never too late to up-level your business.

Mindset: Grow Your People to Grow Your Business

Everyone featured in this book has the same real-world challenges you likely face: ever-shifting regulations, reimbursement cuts, and boom or bust economies. Despite the challenges that come their way, the leaders interviewed here have a People First mindset, which grounds their decisions and ensures they stay on the right path. Embracing People First allows them to grow their business as they grow their people, improving patient outcomes and their bottom line. I want that for you too.

You'll no longer have to ask:

- How do I get people to do what they are supposed to do?
- Why can't I find or keep good people?
- Why don't the managers hold people accountable?

You'll begin to ask the questions that other successful People First leaders ask:

- What is our next opportunity?
- Where do we want to add a location?
- How many new services can we add for our patients?

If you don't agree with the People First mindset, you won't be able to authentically use the communication strategies and behaviors discussed in the chapters to come. People *know* when you don't believe it.

We've all seen organizations that say they care about their team members' professional development but reward only for productivity. They say one thing and then do another, such as, "We want you to have a great employee experience" *but* "we're short-staffed right now, so we'll get back to training when we have enough people to cover the floor." While this type of conflict between what an organization SAYS and what it DOES is common, the disconnect can be corrected by getting clarity on what the organization THINKS.

I've experienced organizations that put *everything* else—including the physical building—ahead of their people. They tend to have the mindset that people are tools or commodities that can be exchanged when things aren't working out. These types of organizations experience higher turnover, difficulty expanding operations, and very low engagement, all of which negatively impact the patient experience. If you view your people as tools, chances are you treat them differently than you would if you saw them as the key to your organizational success.

The first step to a People First mindset is simply to meet people where they are, but simple doesn't always mean easy. The tendency is to want people to already be exactly where you think they should be. Organizations and leaders have been known to get people there by dragging them forward, which only fuels resistance. Instead, help them get to where they need to be by working with them to grow their skills and capabilities.

Think about one of your patients coming in for her third visit. When you review her chart in advance, you know where she should be, so you mentally prepare a treatment plan for the day. But when she walks in, you immediately recognize she isn't where you anticipated she would be. Instead, she's made no progress or, possibly, even regressed. Do you ignore where she is and proceed with the care you planned? Of course not: you meet her where she is.

Don't worry: that doesn't mean you meet your team where they are and then you both stay there. No, you work with them to improve to the level you expect. A People First mindset doesn't ignore the necessity for people to practice at the top of their game. Instead, it provides a framework to grow.

The Career Rock Wall: Advancement versus Growth

In a private practice, there aren't many rungs on the career ladder. And those rungs are far apart in terms of the skills needed to be successful at each level. Thankfully, fostering growth is about creating an environment in which people are encouraged and supported to stretch and reach in ways that don't necessarily adhere to traditional hierarchies.

Shift your organization's mindset from one of advancement via a career ladder to one of continuous growth via a career rock wall. While a career ladder is about titles and job descriptions, a career rock wall is about building experience and developing skills through different "handholds," or projects and activities.

On the career ladder, great clinicians and frontline staff are typically promoted once they've mastered the rung on which they currently stand. However, there is a wide knowledge, skills, and experience gap between a clinician and a leader. And we don't typically teach leadership or management skills until the person has already been promoted to the leadership rung.

CAREER LADDER

CAREER ROCK WALL

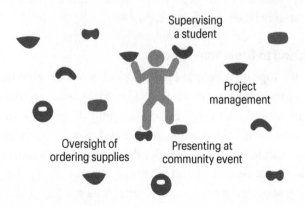

If you've ever seen rock climbing, you know it's necessary to reach for a handhold close to where you are. Sometimes, the move is lateral. Sometimes, the move is upward. And sometimes, it appears as if the move is backward but it's part of a bigger move to get farther ahead. The direction is less important than the skills and experiences collected along the way. On a career rock wall, all of the opportunities for growth and development are in front of the person, just as they are when a person is climbing.

The intention of a career rock wall is to engage people in work that motivates them through activities that build confidence and acumen. A career rock wall is superior to a ladder because it prepares future leaders by training them on the skills and exposing them to the experiences they will need *before* they are thrown into a "higher" position and expected to perform accordingly. People are better equipped to step up and into a leadership role when they've had training in advance.

A career rock wall indicates that an organization has a mindset of continuous learning. The specifics of how to build a career rock wall and set up your team for future success are discussed in more depth in Chapter 8.

Coaching to Grow Your People

Part of adopting a People First mindset is recognizing that people, by nature, want to do good work. A leader's role is to uncover and nurture a person's inherent strengths so they may achieve success at work. To that end, coaching is a leadership mindset and skill set. So, the overall organizational mindset must be that leaders are also coaches. Different from training someone on the requirements for a specific position, coaching is a way of asking questions, building critical thinking skills, and fostering resilience.

One of an organization's imperatives should be to hire leaders with coaching skills or provide training for leaders already on board. Teaching leaders to coach is essential, and if you can't do it personally, bring in outside experts to help develop this critical skill. Design the organization around the philosophy of coaching by prioritizing time and opportunities for coaching to occur, regardless of how busy your practice is.

If you aren't sure a coaching mindset is appropriate or necessary for your organization, consider the growth trajectory of your best performer over several years. Even a strong and long-tenured employee needs to evolve as the organization's needs change.

A further word of caution: if you don't focus on growing your people, you run the risk of getting caught up in an endless cycle of hiring and firing. Even a great candidate with the perfect skills for today's needs could easily be out of date in two years if the organization hasn't invested in their professional growth. This is especially true when the time comes to add managers. If you haven't been growing your people, then no one in-house is ready for a leadership role and you'll have to hire outside the organization.

Mission Reflects Mindset

Each organization is unique, and its mindset is reflected in its mission statement. This key component of THINK guides the SAY and DO for your entire business.

The mission statement is an expression of the organization's purpose. It defines what the organization does and whom it serves; it is the loudest message of intent to the public and the people who work within the company. Your mission statement is a description of your identity, or what you want to be.

Whenever I facilitate team sessions, I always ask people to share the organization's mission with me. And I'm always surprised—though I shouldn't be—that so few people know what theirs is. Even if it's called a "purpose statement," there must be something clear and powerful enough to inspire dedication and commitment from the people whose job it is to deliver on that mission. When the mission statement clearly articulates the "why" of your organization, your people can recite it with feeling because they live it every day in their work.

At Spooner Physical Therapy, a twenty-two-location practice with almost four hundred team members, their core purpose is "Helping people achieve health through movement." This language expresses the company's "why." Julianne Brandt, the chief operating officer, explains that the experience for both patients and team members incorporates the mind, body, and spirit.

Stop here for one minute. Jot down or recite your mission statement right now. If you don't know what it is, why do you get up and go to work every day? Is each day just a series of actions that don't connect to something larger, or is each day part of a chain that builds to a greater purpose? If an organization isn't clear on why it exists, and the people who work there are not connected to that purpose, nothing else matters.

Admittedly, the importance of an organization's mission didn't sink into my own consciousness until I experienced its power firsthand. In 2010, I started working for WellSpan Health in Pennsylvania. Like many organizations, it had an incredibly long mission statement, but no one who worked there knew what it was. It was buried somewhere in the employee handbook, ignored by all.

That year, 2010, was big for organizations and looking ahead. Everyone was building a ten-year plan with the popular and catchy "Vision 2020" tagline. WellSpan Health was no different, and it decided the time was ripe for a new mission. The freshly minted and improved statement was: "Working as one to improve health through exceptional care for all, lifelong wellness, and healthy communities."

At the time, WellSpan Health was in the process of acquiring regional hospitals to bring into the system. We didn't feel unified, but the new mission drove home the point that we were all *one* health system, as opposed to fractured, independent units. Initially, there were eye rolls and a few sarcastic comments about "working as one." Yet, the new mission fulfilled its intention and led the organization toward its new identity.

Over the next seven years, I experienced the power of the words in the new mission statement. They drove our organization forward and became a guiding beacon. People moved from sarcastically remarking, "So much for working as one!" to genuinely saying, "Thanks for working as one on that project," or, "That's a great example of working as one."

The language of *one* infused our systems and thought processes. The weekly leadership call was named the "working as one call." We all knew the intention of the meeting was to keep us updated so we could function together. Since a "working as one" story was always included on the call, people began looking for examples of their team working as one. To this day, I remember every word of WellSpan's mission because it was simple, clear, and applicable. It influenced our behaviors and our attitudes.

While senior leadership had the intention of the organization truly coming together, it didn't happen overnight. Initially, the mission was more of our aspiration than our identity, but over time, it truly reflected WellSpan Health's purpose. It was an expression of leadership's mindset and their intentions in who we served, how we served, and why we served. There was no confusion whatsoever among the staff as to why we came to work each day. That kind of clarity is worth its weight in gold.

Values Guide Behaviors

Just as the mission reveals who you are, the organization's values serve a similar function and ensure your mindset is lived through words and actions. Core values are root beliefs and principles that guide the work.

Many companies simply list words to represent their values: honesty, teamwork, quality, transparency, integrity, and so on. Values need to be more than just words. They need to have definitions and behavioral examples to eliminate misinterpretation of the organization's beliefs and philosophies. Take the time to connect the words to principles so everyone is guided by the same overarching ideals.

Values help shape the culture and drive decision making. They provide clarity on expected behaviors and actions, and become the moral compass for every individual in the organization. In fact, they are the internal beacon for the organization's SAY and DO.

At Spooner Physical Therapy, not only did the senior leadership team take the time to clarify their mindset and intentions through a succinct purpose statement, but they also worked with other team members to craft a treatment philosophy statement and a core values blueprint. More than just lists of words or phrases, the blueprint defines behaviors that demonstrate the organization's values and treatment philosophy.

Intention: Set the Course of Action

Our intentions are the overarching aims that set the course of our actions. Intentions are communicated through the policies, procedures, and processes to get work done. Because intentions shape our words (SAY) and our actions (DO), it's important to be crystal clear on your intentions for specific activities.

> Intentions are the overarching aims that set the course of our actions.

How often do you review your intentions and confirm that your organizational policies, procedures, and processes match those intentions? Many of the conversations I have with my clients begin with me asking, "What is the intention of that activity?" I'm often met with a blank stare, or several starts and stops as they try to articulate it. Very few organizations have a method in place to review their mindset and intentions, and that needs to change.

The Huddle Muddle

One company I worked with needed help with their communication strategy. The owner had read that huddles were a great communication tool, so he implemented them daily. (We'll explore why huddles are effective and how to get the most out of them in Chapter 5.) After a few months, the owner said he was thinking about getting rid of them. The huddles took close to thirty minutes, everyone looked bored, few people actually contributed, and even the leaders couldn't see the value.

When I asked the leadership team the intention of the huddle, I immediately recognized the problem had nothing to do with the huddle itself. One person said huddles were a way to get the team excited for the day. Another said it was to review what had happened the day before, and a third person thought they were to address problems with work progression. If only you could have seen the leaders' faces during our conversation. One of them even asked the others, "Wait! What did you think huddles were for?" The intention wasn't clear to the leaders, so how could the huddle be effective for the team? Asking, "What's the intention?" led to clarity and a new design that then led to successful and productive huddles.

Imagine the effects when this same question is applied to other activities within the business! You'll have an opportunity to explore this question and experience firsthand how it helps improve your systems and processes in the Self-Check experiment at the end of this chapter.

Leadership Team Alignment: A Commitment to Mindset and Intentions

The huddle story highlights the need for every member of the leadership team to be on the same page with the organization's mindset and intentions. There are plenty of analogies and metaphors for team alignment in management circles, but one of my favorites occurs in nature. During migration, geese fly in an ideal formation for efficiency. The V shape they naturally fall into reduces wind resistance, which allows the flock to conserve energy and keep track of every bird in the group. They each assume a slightly different position, but the overall shape keeps them aligned.

I want your organization to experience the natural harmony and efficiency that geese experience in their flight pattern. Each person contributes to the overall picture. Their contribution is aligned with the work of others because everyone is aligned with the organization's mindset and intentions. When conflict arises or tough decisions need to be made, alignment keeps the conversations productive and moving forward.

Contrast that type of momentum and synergy with a group that is not aligned with the big picture. Think of the wasted energy when someone's work needs to be redone because it doesn't connect to other people's work. As you walk the People First path, an effective and efficient operation in which everyone is moving in the same direction is the result of a leadership team that is aligned on THINK, SAY, DO, and GROW.

Misalignment and the Depth of Its Damage

Be forewarned: there will undoubtedly be a few individuals who are not aligned with a People First mindset, even among the leadership team. When that occurs, it will become necessary to invite those individuals to leave the organization. If the idea of asking someone to leave because they aren't on board with a People First mindset makes you uncomfortable, think about the longer-term struggles you'll face as a result of the doubters. Disagreement on behaviors and language are to be expected, but a firm commitment to mindset and intentions is required.

I know a practice owner whose mantra has always been "People First." His business was incredibly successful financially; he had great retention rates and high patient satisfaction scores. When the time came to hire a new chief financial officer, he found someone he thought was a brilliant candidate. Once he was part of the organization, though, it became clear the new CFO didn't align with a People First mindset. He pushed for astronomical productivity levels, changed volume requirements before new people could be added to the team, and engaged in several activities that put finance before people.

The entire organization felt different—in a bad way. After eleven months, the owner finally asked the CFO to leave. Those eleven months were painful for the team: people started to leave, the company attracted fewer applicants, and the staff discontent trickled down to patients.

Unfortunately, and as is often the case, the organization didn't instantly realign after the CFO's departure. It took several more months for the company to rebuild trust with the staff and reorient around the People First mindset. I share this real-life cautionary tale to illustrate how one bad apple can spoil the barrel, even when the entire organization is built on the mindset of putting its people first.

Redesign and the Roots of Resistance

While the CFO in the story was driven by finance over people, understand that what seems like resistance to the People First mindset may just be resistance to the way information is presented. It's your job as leader to determine the root cause of the resistance.

Imagine the following scenario. Susan and Bob are two very skilled leaders on your team. They are both committed to the People First mindset, but when you start to redesign your organization, they have very different reactions.

Susan is motivated by new ideas and different ways of doing things. When the organization looks at restructuring the performance review process, she jumps at the chance to start from scratch. She is known as an out-of-the-box thinker and gets excited when she hears, "We're going to try something different."

Bob is driven by proven methods and traditional ways of doing things. The idea of starting from scratch irritates him. He is more comfortable relying on the "way things have been done in the past." He recognizes that not everything about the current process supports the People First mindset, but he doesn't want to throw away all the systems the organization has been using. His resistance causes him to appear as a naysayer for the People First path. He isn't. Building on proven methods motivates him, and out-of-the-box changes frustrate him.

Bob and Susan are in agreement that the current performance review process doesn't match the organization's intentions. They simply disagree on how to make changes.

Taking the time to understand what motivates individuals on your team will allow you to see the root cause of their resistance or excitement and move closer to leadership team alignment. Resistance to the "why" is different from resistance to the "how." The latter resistance can lead to better solutions, but only if everyone is in agreement with the purpose and intentions behind the work.

The challenge with THINK is that it is not tangible; what we DO and SAY are the tangible expressions of the organization's mindset and intentions. Acknowledge this reality, and get clear on your organization's THINK. Nothing is more important than this first foundational rock. Your organization's THINK is revealed through the words and actions we will explore in the coming chapters. THINK is the stepping stone for everything else that comes on the People First path.

Self-Check: Intentions in Action

Remember how asking "What's the intention?" brought clarity to the huddle muddle? This Self-Check offers a chance to articulate your intentions behind different activities and confirm that others see and understand it the same way. The goal here is alignment.

Start with a list of activities your organization practices and state the intentions behind them. Next, have the entire leadership team repeat the exercise. This will help you clearly see where there is agreement on and/or confusion about intentions, and it highlights where communication needs to be improved.

In the following grid, I've provided a few activities, processes, and procedures to get you started. Don't stop with these examples; build your own complete list. THINK carefully about the intention of each and record your answers. Survey your team and get their input as well.

Activity/Process/Procedure	Intention
Onboarding	
Corrective Action	
Dress Code	
Absentee Policy	

Let's take a closer look at dress code, which can be a hot topic and point of contention in an organization. To dig into the intention behind a dress code, ask: Why do you have the dress code you have? What's the point?

- Because you like polo shirts, so everyone should like polo shirts?
- Because you think street clothes look messy?
- Because safety requirements specify a certain type of footwear?
- Because you want people to have the individual freedom to wear whatever they want?
- Because you want your organization to reflect a standard of professionalism?

Once everything is out on the table, true dialogue can begin. Make sure the intentions are clearly understood, and adjust activities as needed. Sometimes, the act of stating your intentions provides enough of a backstory to clear up any confusion. This list of activities and their intentions plays a crucial role in what we SAY and DO, the next two rocks in the People First cairn.

3

The THINK
Leadership Factor

ONE OF MY clients was struggling in her supervisor role. She wanted to be a good leader and worked hard to learn about leadership SAY and DO. She believed that if she had the right words and actions in her arsenal, she could get her team to perform the way she wanted them to. Her THINK, however, remained fixed on the patient experience—so much so that she put the patients' needs ahead of her team's needs. Frustrated, the team began to act out. After some discussion, she was forthcoming in saying, "I can't help it. The patient is my ultimate concern."

There is absolutely nothing wrong with having a patient first mindset. The difficulty comes when you attempt *to lead other people* with that mindset. Ultimately, my client recognized she had the power to choose where to put her energy. Despite her best intentions, the People First mindset that is necessary to lead others went against her grain. So, she found a direct patient care role where she could truly thrive and remain committed to her inherent nature.

Like my client, you have choices too. If you're an owner and you love your role as a clinician, then continue treating patients and hire leaders to lead. A few of the practice owners I've worked with have said, "I like patient care, but I want to focus on building the business," or, "I love watching others grow so I focus on being a People First leader." Understanding what you *want* to do, as well as your natural strengths, helps you know where to focus your time and energy and allows you to authentically embrace a role that makes the most sense for you. When you are in authentic alignment with your THINK, your leadership SAY and DO will ring true.

On the People First path, leadership THINK is "people before patients." If you are meeting your team's needs, they can meet the patients' needs. Overlooking your people leads to the negative outcomes previously discussed. Here are some key findings that reveal the negative impact of poor leadership on productivity, tenure, and patient satisfaction.

- CustomInsight discovered that "five of the top ten drivers of disengagement relate to my manager."[1]

- People who rate their supervisor's performance poorly are four times more likely to be job hunting.[2]

- Fifty-four percent of employees have left a job because of their manager.[3]

Many leadership books tell us how to do things, but if we don't start with mindset and intentions, we can't successfully carry out the "how." This chapter is the chance to examine your leadership mindset and intentions in detail.

The Impact of Mindset on Leadership

My own leadership transformation came after I got to a place where I didn't trust myself or anyone else. My confidence was shaken to its core. I thought I was doing what a good leader should do, but I was blind to my gaps. It took losing a job to force me to reexamine my approach. I hope you never have to lose it all or go through a personal tragedy to have an "aha" moment. I share mine here in the hope you can avoid the same missteps I took.

Default Mindset: A Tale of Two Storms

When I led Acute Care, as mentioned earlier, my default priority was patient first. Despite the fact that I wasn't treating patients on a regular basis, it was hard to see my job through any other lens.

At one point, there was a terrible flood in the area. As the rain poured down and the rivers overflowed their banks, the staff worried about their homes. I expected everyone to remain at work, or make it in for their upcoming shifts. I showed no compassion for them or empathy about their concerns.

Someone remarked, "We're not essential, and I need to take care of my basement." Her comment was an emotional trigger for me. We absolutely were essential. To say we weren't was another example of the staff denigrating our profession. Because my emotional intelligence was low, I wasn't even aware that her words were a trigger. My lack of self-awareness meant I certainly couldn't regulate my behavior.

The flood was the beginning of the end of my time with that team. They came to work but they were frustrated and angry. They brought their hands but not their hearts or minds.

Four years later, when I was serving as the operations administrator in Urgent Care for the medical group, our town had a massive snowstorm, larger than we'd experienced in years. Only a few of the roads were plowed, and even those were treacherous. Urgent Care had to remain open because our services were vital to the community.

Because of what I learned during the flood, I took a different approach to staying open. With a mindset focused on the people who worked in Urgent Care (instead of the people who might need care), we called every team member to see what their situation was. We offered rides to staff if they couldn't access their cars, and we understood if they couldn't get out in four feet of snow. My emotional intelligence was high enough by then for me to feel real empathy for each individual. I also had a heightened awareness about what might trigger an emotional response and was ready to self-regulate.

We opened only our largest location, but patients could receive care. More importantly, it became a turning point in how people viewed the leadership team. We demonstrated a People First mindset, and they rewarded us with higher levels of engagement, increased productivity, and a better patient experience.

We all have a default mindset. It exists without conscious thought. Some people naturally look at tasks first, while others naturally start with people. When it comes to decision making, healthcare practice owners and leaders typically have one of three defaults: Finance, Patients, or People.

What is your default? Whatever it is, it's OK as long as you are willing to stop, take stock, and consciously shift your thinking. THINK leadership asks that you override your brain's preselected default and explore different ways of looking at the challenges and problems your organization faces—ways that consider your people and their needs at work. Let's explore some of the various "minds" within THINK leadership and see how they blend to create the mind of a People First leader.

The Curious Mind

There is a common misconception that leaders need to be experts in all areas of their business. Many owners think they have to fix everything themselves, which is a pressure cooker mindset that quickly leads to burnout.

My clients who were interviewed for this book don't assume they have all the answers. These outstanding leaders are continuous learners and seek to understand multiple perspectives. Instead of trying to solve all of the problems on their own, they've learned how to ask powerful questions (Chapter 6), listen for meaning (Chapter 6), collaborate to develop a plan (Chapter 7), and then experiment with new solutions (Chapter 11).

Get curious: with a beginner's mindset, examine the work that happens within your organization. Imagine you're walking into the practice for the first time. What do you see? Who can help you understand what is happening every day? What is the general mood of the place?

The LEAN methodology for continuous improvement suggests that leaders "Go to the Gemba." In Japanese, the literal meaning of *Gemba* is "the actual place." In LEAN, "Go to the Gemba" means "go see, ask why, and show respect." It's about going to the source; so if you're curious about how a new process is working, go to where the process actually happens. Talk to the people who are responsible for executing it. Are there flaws or hiccups? What's working well, and what needs to be improved? Likewise, if you want to improve inter-actions with patients at the front desk, go to the waiting room and see what happens there. Ask the intake person how flow could be improved. What is the average patient wait time? How could the experience be made more enjoyable?

Curiosity is about learning new information, not sharing what you know. Engage your team to find solutions, and seek guidance from others. Refrain from suggesting your own solutions on the spot. You won't have enough information to wade in after only one or two observations. A truly curious leader can let go of their assumptions about the "right" way to do things and be open to suggestions, feedback, and observa-tions from the people on the ground. A leader with a curious mind will have a greater breadth of information from which to make decisions, and will most likely enjoy the exploration process. Go see what's out there and what your people have to say about it.

The Grateful Mind

Be grateful. No matter what challenges you face, look for the silver lining. Even on your worst day, find one thing to be grateful for. When you seek things to be grateful for, you'll notice opportunities for gratitude everywhere. The more you experience it, the more it comes to you. It's like when you buy a new car and suddenly you see the same make and model on every street.

Be thankful not only for what goes well, but also for what doesn't go well. All organizations must experiment with trial and error to figure out what works. A misstep, a weak process, or errors in the system are all opportunities for learning and improvement. Recognizing those opportunities and finding new solutions are moments to be grateful for.

Leaders who have a grateful mind know the importance of sharing gratitude with others. Take the time to thank the people who help your business function every day. Look for the good things your team is doing and acknowledge them. It doesn't need to be a big sweeping accomplishment; everyday behaviors and attitudes deserve thanks too. Find ways to celebrate large and small events.

The Humble Mind

One of my mentors always says, "Hubris before the fall." Hubris is overconfidence in or arrogance about one's abilities, and it can be a very dangerous headspace. Excessive pride prevents us from being curious; it prevents us from seeing value in other people's ideas and opinions. It's OK to be proud of what you've accomplished, but don't let that pride get blown out of proportion.

Humility is the opposite of hubris, and it's a mindset worth cultivating. Being humble means being modest about your own importance. There's a well-known but unattributed quote that speaks to the power of a humble mind: "Humility is not thinking less of yourself, it's thinking of yourself less."

Many of the leaders I work with express frustration when they can't get people to do what they are supposed to do. They talk about holding them accountable, or finding some way to let them know they're not carrying their weight. In their book *How Did That Happen?*, Roger Connors and Tom Smith say before you attempt to hold someone else accountable, hold yourself accountable first. They suggest reframing the question from "How did that happen?" to "How did *I* let that happen?"[4]

Be willing to take responsibility for mistakes that happen on your watch and recognize that we're all human, and we all make mistakes. A humble mindset is a real equalizer and makes you a more accessible, approachable, and relatable leader.

The Willing Mind

When one of my clients was facing a sticky situation with his fellow practice owners, he asked me if he could just go stick his head in the sand rather than deal with the issue. We both laughed, but he was only half joking. There will always be times when we'd like to ignore the tough stuff, pull the covers over our heads, and hope it all goes away.

Leaders with a willing mind know they need to put all the issues on the table so they can be resolved instead of letting them fester under the surface. As tempting as it may be to ignore, avoid, or even deny a problem, the fastest course to moving forward is to look it square in the eye and deal with it. I'm not suggesting that leaders start attacking all the tough stuff in their organization like a bull in a china shop. People First leaders, who are anchored to organizational THINK, are willing to engage in and address challenges while also focusing on the needs and experiences of other people. They are also willing to do whatever it takes to support their team.

A client and I were prepping for a difficult conversation with one of his staff about gaps in performance. I asked him how committed he was to helping the person achieve the improvements necessary to remain part of the team. He gave the question some thought and responded honestly, "Amy, I know this isn't the answer I'm supposed to give, but I'm only 85% committed to helping this person."

My client's willingness to be honest with himself gave him the opportunity to make a choice. I then asked if he was 100% willing to go into the conversation with a curious mind to learn about the employee's perspective. He agreed to do so. The result was a collaborative conversation during which they were able to find solutions. I attribute that success primarily to his willingness to be curious. It paid off, and they were able to move forward.

The Pilot's Mind

Did you know that airplanes fly off course 90% of the time? I was fascinated to learn this information. Weather, turbulence, and other atmospheric factors shift the plane away from the destination.

Think about this from the pilot's perspective. He or she sets the course and then, instead of sitting back confident that the plane will arrive perfectly as planned, spends the entire flight making micro-adjustments to bring the plane back on track. Instead of getting frustrated with the disturbances, they focus on the destination. They accept, in advance, that the journey won't be perfect. Instead of fighting that knowledge, they fight the challenges as they arise, constantly and calmly.

It is a leader's job to set the course: the vision, the goals, and the nonnegotiable rules of the practice. Just like a pilot facing obstacles in the sky, leaders can't prevent their people from veering slightly off course. They must work with them to get back on track. Bringing team members back into alignment taps into the skills of a pilot's mind.

Using a slightly different metaphor, my colleague says her role is to provide her team with a plumb line. These vertical reference points ensure a structure is centered. She keeps her people centered by communicating clear policies, guidelines, and expectations. She knows they will occasionally fall out of alignment; her job is to help them get back in balance.

A leader with a pilot's mind is constantly looking at the view ahead and the factors that could impact the flight course. By being alert and aware, pilot leaders make frequent adjustments to ensure the destination is reached safely and successfully.

The Coach's Mind

The Co-Active Coaching Model asserts, "People are naturally creative, resourceful and whole."[5] When leaders view people as whole, they don't view them as broken or needing to be fixed. They don't blame people when they falter and assume they are bad or lazy. They recognize that people simply need to be supported and guided on their path.

Daniel Goleman, Richard Boyatzis, and Annie McKee's bestselling book, *Primal Leadership*, presents six dominant leadership styles in business. The authors say that of the six, "despite the commonly held belief that every leader needs to be a good coach, leaders tend to exhibit this style least often."[6]

Understanding the intention of coaching is a critical precursor to learning how to coach. Yes, coaching is intended to improve overall job performance, but at its heart, coaching is about professional development. Everyone, regardless of their title, level of experience, or job history, stands to benefit from professional development. Therefore, coaching should not be reserved for people who are struggling. It is also necessary for people who are excelling. You may have a rising star far exceeding expectations. You don't want to slow their trajectory by

> At its heart, coaching is about professional development.

assuming they have everything they need. Instead, you meet them where they are, and help them continue to accelerate.

Can you see how these aspects all blend together? For example, a humble mind recognizes that there is more to learn and is willing to ask for help. And that curiosity helps realign the plane on its journey, which creates a sense of gratitude when back on track.

The Balancing Act: How Many Hats Are You Wearing?

Throughout the day, leaders are often required to shift roles. Sometimes they have to wear the hat of an owner, a leader, and a clinician all within an eight-hour time frame. It's important to be clear on what role you're playing at any given moment so you can adjust your mindset and intentions to best serve the role.

When treating, your intention is excellent patient care. How do you remember to take off the clinician hat when a team member needs your attention as the business owner? It's not an easy balancing act.

One of my clients told me he had to delay implementing some new programs because he was treating 80% of the time. I could see this loop playing out forever unless he made a change. Once he cut back on treatment to focus on business demands and the team's needs, his therapists stepped up to fill in the gap. He was able to devote time to carefully selecting and truly aligning new team members, which allowed him to move forward with those programs.

Another client experienced the opposite situation. When treating patients, she found herself looking at the other therapists' notes or treatment plans to assess what additional training they needed and whether their plans were compliant. She had to consciously reset her default mindset from People First to patient first, so she could tend to the person in front of her.

Because THINK is the first foundation rock in the People First cairn, leaders need to be aware of how many roles (and rocks) they're trying to balance at once. Although this book is about building a People First organization, with the mindset and intentions to match, I recognize that different roles require different hats. Be aware of which one you're wearing throughout your day, and which mindset and intentions you're bringing to your interactions.

Intentions Determine the Experience

In Chapter 2, we briefly spoke about intentions in the context of organizational design. Now, let's examine how intentions play out in the leadership realm. Specifically, how do your systems, processes, or procedures reflect your aims? Are those systems, processes, and procedures achieving what you intend?

For the sake of illustration, we'll review three common business processes and look at how a leader's intentions shape the experience and their effectiveness: performance reviews, corrective action, and termination.

Performance reviews are often viewed as a step that must be taken—a box to be checked—to determine if someone is eligible for a raise. If your intention is to "get through it and get it over with," you'll probably move through the process as quickly as possible. Or maybe you'll put off the reviews as long as possible because they're not a priority. Maybe you'll even skip scheduling a discussion with the person and simply send an informal, impersonal review over for their signature.

What if, instead, the intention of performance reviews was to confirm or regain your people's alignment, celebrate success, and adjust their learning and development plan? Imagine how those intentions would change your words and actions during the process. You'd stop delaying them. You'd dedicate time to them. You'd ask questions and seek to understand.

The overall experience of performance reviews is vastly different depending on the intention. That same scenario is at play with virtually every single process or system within your organization. How do *you* want to experience activities, and, just as importantly, how do you want *others* to experience them?

Corrective action is another example of how intentions drive word choice and behavior. When someone needs to be written up, are you documenting the interaction for Human Resources? If so, why? Is it because you want to be compliant with rules and regulations? Are you trying to protect yourself from being sued if you need to fire someone?

Instead, what if your intention for corrective action was to support and coach the person toward improvement? What if the necessity for corrective action could be used as a learning opportunity? Think about how different the experience would be for both you and the person in the hot seat.

Another example of how intentions determine the experience of an activity is termination. If your mindset is that people are whole, then you recognize that the employee isn't a bad person even though it might be necessary to let them go. Your organization simply isn't the right place for them.

In a now offline article called "Project Freedom (or: Liberate Your Low Performers)," Sebastian Thrun, founder and chairman of Udacity, memorably wrote, "My foremost responsibility as a manager is to build up my people. Letting them go is a matter of last resort." If you've done all you can to support and coach a team member, and the person is still underperforming, consider what might be holding them back. No one wants to fail. Helping someone realize they're not in the right place can actually be a relief. If a situation isn't working, it's as hard on the employee as it is on the manager.

No one wants to fail.

Thrun also wrote, "The key to Project Freedom is to stop thinking about yourself and instead to focus on what's best for your people. So, ask yourself whether someone would be better off on a different team or at a different company."

Liberating low performers is aligned with the People First mindset on a few levels: First, if someone is unable to thrive within your organization, they're likely not aligned with your THINK. They will be happier in a different environment where they can experience common ground. Second, it also demonstrates that you recognize the individual's impact on the rest of team. Avoiding a necessary termination can cause the people who are performing to feel demoralized and disengaged. Put *all* of your people first by kindly showing the low performers the door.

The Happiness By-Product

It would be a mistake to think the People First mindset and intentions are about making people happy, although happiness can certainly be a by-product. Happiness is a feeling in the moment, and the fact is, not all business decisions will feel good to everyone. But if hard decisions are put in a People First context, the team will trust your leadership because they know you want the best for them.

Mike Johnson, practice president of BAYADA Health Home Care, is the epitome of a People First leader. He is quick to point out that his job is to lead, not to make everyone happy. He, and every other People First leader in this book, must make tough business decisions, and, yes, even Mike has received an angry email from a team member. As a People First leader, he cultivates a level of open dialogue through his leadership style. He also recognizes that he can't change a business decision for one out of three thousand people's needs.

People incorrectly assume that People First leadership means creating an environment in which people are allowed to slack off or aren't challenged to be their best. As you've realized by this point in the book, this assumption couldn't be further from the truth.

People First leadership is about serving the team by setting clear expectations, skillfully navigating productive conflict, and coaching individuals to be their best. It's about being a living embodiment of your THINK, reflected through mindset, intentions, and leadership team alignment. These foundational elements provide the base on which everything else in your organization rests.

Self-Check: What's Your Mindset?

You have choices. The ability to choose comes after awareness of your current state of mind. Once you understand that, you can decide what to focus on next.

Start with a self-check on your default mindset. Remember, we don't control that first unconscious thought, so don't try to ignore it. Recognize your default, and if not People First, make a conscious choice to shift your mindset.

Once you are clear on your mindset, take a look at the other aspects of a People First leader's mind. Over the course of a day or week, track the percent of time you maintain these different aspects. Then consider ways to increase your focus and skill at shifting your thinking.

	Percent of Time	Ways to Increase the Percent
The Curious Mind		
The Grateful Mind		
The Humble Mind		
The Willing Mind		
The Pilot's Mind		
The Coach's Mind		

TWO

SAY

4

The Weight of Words

ITH YOUR MINDSET and intentions well established, let's move along the People First path to the next rock in your organizational cairn: SAY. The focus shifts from what you THINK to the language attached to various roles and activities within your practice.

The SAY and DO rocks are deeply interrelated. Sometimes, words will lead while your organizational design behaviors catch up. Other times, your organization will demonstrate behaviors but the language lags behind. That's OK. In fact, it's why I suggest you read the entire book before deciding where you want to start experimenting.

What's in a Name?

Have you ever seen or heard something's name and been confused because the name simply doesn't match the thing? I remember going to a place called Turtle Beach only to discover there hadn't been turtles on the beach for over fifty years. The misnaming caused me some disappointment: I wanted to see turtles!

Think about the names you attach to the roles, activities, and processes within your practice, and their implications. Do those names reflect your organizational intentions?

Job Titles: Go Beyond Lip Service

Every role in your organization has a name, or a job title, from the practice manager to the care coordinator. Job titles are an expression of the intentions for the role. They have the power to determine how someone behaves as well as how they are treated by others, both internally and externally.

Apple's tech support, named Genius, is a good example. When I walk into an Apple store and ask for a Genius, I'm confident that person will have the answer. They're geniuses, after all, and if they can't fix my problem, no one can. "Genius" is a genius name for tech support. It inspires confidence in the consumer who needs their help, and it elevates the people in those positions.

Let's look at the front desk position in a healthcare practice. I've seen the role named everything from First Impression Officer, to Registrar, to Physician Office Assistant. As you read those different titles, do you get an idea of what the person in the role actually does? From the outside looking in, there's a lot of room for speculation.

"First Impression Officer" makes me think the person's job is to make patients feel good when they come into the practice. "Registrar" makes me think of someone typing reports and managing files. I can't guess what a "Physician Office Assistant" does, but it's probably a wide range of things.

Now, think about what type of applicant each of these titles attracts. What qualifications, skill sets, or personality traits might the different titles subconsciously indicate?

Remember, all three titles represent the same job, but a registrar may have a different social interaction style from a first impressions officer. When someone looks for a new job, titles attract different types of people.

I had the opportunity to work with the leadership team from Choice Therapy in Minnesota. When Mya, the director of culture, first reached out, I wondered if her role was truly related to culture operations or if it was just a cleverly disguised name for Human Resources. Turns out, Mya really was their beacon of culture. The leadership team loved her spirit; they recognized her passion to support the team and build the culture. Mya got to pick her title and, she said, that it's made all the difference. She used her title to express her intentions for the role. It's become a powerful reminder of the key accountability she has within the organization.

Titles can breed confusion or create clarity; they can inspire action or annoy. What do your job titles do? You'll have the opportunity to dig into this in the Self-Check at the end of the chapter.

Improvement Plans without Plans for Improvement?

The same level of confusion can apply to organizational processes. For example, I worked with a client who used something called "PIPs." No one outside the organization would know what a PIP is, but they told me it's an acronym for Performance Improvement Plan. I thought, "Great! I love it," and imagined a carefully crafted plan for each team member's development and improvement. When I asked if everyone in the organization had a PIP and how they were updated, laughter ensued.

Turns out, PIPs have very little to do with improvement, despite the word being part of the acronym. A PIP is the document the organization uses to write someone up during the corrective action process, and it's often a precursor to termination. It's primarily about what someone did wrong; only a very small section of the document covers improvement. Not surprisingly, no one wanted a PIP. Make sure your terminology is accurate to avoid misinterpretation.

Scoreboards and Scorecards: People Are Not Data Points

Scoreboards and scorecards are another example of nomenclature's importance in communicating an activity's intention. I'm a huge fan of the book *The 4 Disciplines of Execution*, by Chris McChesney, Sean Covey, and Jim Huling. When referring to the benefits of an organizational scoreboard, the authors say that when keeping score, people play differently. Scoring breeds a competitive spirit, which is appropriate in certain situations.[1]

In football, you get a quick snapshot of how the teams are doing because the scoreboard is visible to all, up to date, and shows only the high-level metrics of winning. Scoreboards provide a snapshot of the entire game. It not about a specific player; it's about the whole team.

While I agree with the idea of a scoreboard for the organization, there are two reasons I don't have the same level of confidence in scorecards for individuals. First, scorecards are only about "the numbers." They can't fully reflect the entire picture of exceptional performance. People quickly, and justifiably, grow frustrated when their contributions are distilled down to a few data points. Scorecards remind me of the vital signs portion on a patient's chart. Yes, numbers are an essential starting point. They give clues as to where you might need to focus more deeply, but they aren't the whole story.

Second, if a person is judged only on their scorecard, how does such a process impact the team dynamic? It creates an environment in which people are primarily concerned about themselves and their own performance, which is the opposite of how healthcare should function. Someone who is succeeding should be encouraged to help someone who is lagging behind, not leave them in the dust.

If one of my clients wants to use scorecards, I encourage them to use metrics that foster a collaborative mindset and tie the whole team together. For example, arrival rates are an appropriate shared metric because multiple people are responsible for getting patients to keep their appointments.

The intention of scorecards is usually to get everyone on the same page and performing at their highest level, but they tend to have the opposite effect. Plus, the very name—scorecard—can send a negative message to team members. Very few people in healthcare are driven only by scores and motivated by competition; the others just feel alienated and annoyed.

Nomenclature failing to align with intention happens throughout organizational design, and it creates unnecessary confusion. Are you unintentionally sowing discord through poor word choice? THINK about what you SAY and how you SAY it.

The Employee Lifecycle:
A Picture Is Worth a Thousand Words

For years, I used the standard nomenclature associated with the employee lifecycle: recruit, onboard, and retain. When I changed the words associated with each stage of the lifecycle, a seismic shift occurred for me. It was the "aha" moment that started me down the People First path.

While a picture is worth a thousand words, the words in the graphic shared here are pure gold. They represent my dream that every healthcare organization will be a place where people can thrive; where every phase of the employee lifecycle will be redesigned to reveal people's true potential. My intention of helping individuals and organizations grow is embedded in the language of its processes.

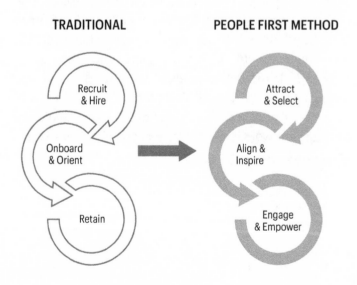

TRADITIONAL	PEOPLE FIRST METHOD
Recruit & Hire	Attract & Select
Onboard & Orient	Align & Inspire
Retain	Engage & Empower

When I started to share this graphic in presentations, I saw people light up. They instantly recognized the positive difference the words had in how they felt about the lifecycle. Language not only reframes what each stage is called but it begins the transformation of how the activities within each stage are carried out. Let's briefly examine each of the three phases here, and later, in Part Three: DO, I'll cover each phase in much greater detail.

Attract and Select versus Recruit and Hire

Wouldn't you love to have a line of people out the door who want to come work for you? Well, that's possible.

I remember meeting a bus inspector on a plane a few years ago. During the two-hour flight, he spent most of the time talking about how great his company was. He explained that it took him two years and three separate applications to finally land a job with this amazing company. Friends who already worked there told him how great it was. He knew it was hard to get hired because turnover was very low. But he kept trying, and now that he was in, he'd never leave.

The man's story illustrates the vast difference between recruiting and attracting. When your brand is strongly tied to being a great place to work, you attract talented people who are willing to do what it takes to work at your company. They aren't just looking for a job; they are looking for a career with your organization. If you've attracted them, they know they are lucky to have been selected and will work harder to be successful. They are committed to the organization before they even have the job offer in hand. If people are attracted to your business, you won't even need to "recruit."

Align and Inspire versus Onboard and Orient

The words "onboarding" and "orientation" always seem to be intermingled, so I did a little research as to why. Onboarding is "management jargon first created in the 1970s that refers to the mechanism through which new employees acquire the necessary knowledge, skills, and behaviors in order to become effective organizational members."[2] The Society for Human Resource Management (SHRM) explains that onboarding is "integrating a new employee with a company and its culture, as well as getting a new hire the tools and information needed."[3] SHRM also describes onboarding as "acclimating" someone to the new job.

Merriam-Webster defines "orient" as such: "to direct toward the interests of a particular group; to set or arrange in any determinant position."[4] And SHRM defines it as the paperwork and tasks to complete the hiring process.

Definitions aside, onboarding and orientation are seen as checklists—a roster of competencies and paperwork that need to be filled out to get someone safely up and running. Of course, bringing on a new team member must include the practical and tactical items that allow them to perform their job safely, but is that the only goal? Of course not.

The People First approach sees this phase as an opportunity to inspire new team members about the work they'll be doing. Part of that includes getting them aligned with the team, the culture, the organizational goals, and the overall experience of the workplace environment. Shift your intention of orientation through a checklist of tasks to the alignment of head, heart, and hands for the job ahead.

Engage and Empower versus Retain

Let's examine the definition of each of these three words and the different feelings they evoke.

- **RETAIN:** keep possession of; keep in one's service by paying.[5]

- **ENGAGE:** having full attention, being fully occupied, focused, and involved.[6]

- **EMPOWER:** to give someone the official authority, or the freedom or confidence to do something.[7]

The ideal employment arrangement isn't about possessing the people who work for you. It's about giving them the freedom, confidence, and tools to be fully involved in the work at hand.

Remember the bus inspector I met on the plane? Do you think he was attracted to the organization he worked for because it successfully "retained" his friends? No! People are attracted to organizations because of the opportunity to be engaged in the work.

Engaged employees tell me that their organization gives them the autonomy to do what they do best. Leaders trust that their team members are professionals and will get things done in a way that is aligned with the organization's core values and mission. This is the crux of it all!

Words set the tone for the organization, ensuring that every team member is on the same page about the intentions and mindset for organizational activities. Carefully consider how words and names impact people's impressions. Unfortunately, traditional nomenclature is so embedded in our vernacular, most leaders don't even think about how it's interpreted.

My world tilted on its axis the day that I replaced the traditional words in the employee lifecycle with new words that properly represent the intention and purpose of each stage. Suddenly, I saw in color what had previously been black and white. This one small act made a huge difference and opened up a world of possibility, and the People First path began to crystalize in my mind. It led me to a deeper consideration of communication and our systems of SAY within the business, covered in the next chapter. I hope the words associated with People First have the same effect on you.

Self-Check: Call It What It Is

Healthcare is littered with jargon and abbreviations, which often distracts from the true meaning of the words associated with specific activities. For the purpose of appreciating the power of language, especially as it relates to behaviors, focus on the full name for different activities within your practice as opposed to shorthand or acronyms. (Recall the PIP.)

For this experiment, look at all the job titles in your organization plus your activities and intentions list from Chapter 2. Ask yourself, and your team, if the name of the role and/or the activity is aligned with the intention.

Have fun with this, but be careful how far off the track you go from clarity. What do the names Operations Ninja, Happiness Hero, or Brand Warrior really do, aside from get a brief chuckle? When you start to see titles such as Herder of Helpless People, fun with nomenclature has gone off the rails. You don't want people to laugh because the name is absurd.

A medical assistant is a certified position known to the public. For clarity's sake, simply call that person a medical assistant. Don't make up a name that no one will understand or that creates a false impression of what they do. I recall seeing someone's title was Director of Details, which I thought was wonderful. I knew exactly what she did and wanted to hire someone like that for my own company.

If your intentions don't match the name, what might be more suitable?

JOB TITLES		
Current Name	Intention	Updated Name
Scheduler	Coordinate multiple appointments	Care Coordinator

ACTIVITIES, PROCESSES, AND PROCEDURES	
Activity/Process/Procedure	Intention
Annual Review	
Improvement Plan	
Dress Code	

5

Systems for Communication and Connection

SAY IS NOT only about what words we use in our organizational design. It's also about when and how we communicate with the team. We will explore the way an organization communicates as a whole and how that communication strategy, or lack thereof, becomes the system of SAY for your organizational design.

To emphasize the importance of systems of SAY, consider a few stats from Dynamic Signal's 2019 *State of Employee Communication and Engagement Study.*[1]

- Eighty percent of the US workforce reports feeling stressed because of ineffective company communication.

- Ninety percent of employees say good company communication is key to a positive working environment.

- Fifty-two percent of employees said they had witnessed poor financial outcomes due to poor communication.

Beyond these data points, think about how your communication system can prevent safety errors, misunderstandings, and frustration.

The System of SAY: How Do You Communicate?

SAY requires just as much attention to detail as every other part of your organizational design. Be thoughtful, intentional, and consistent in how it is used. A poorly balanced system creates confusion, fear, anxiety, errors, and unresolved conflict. The primary intention of communication is clarity and connection. The outcomes can vary from a simple exchange of information to behavioral changes or alignment with an idea or process. These goals and intentions are more easily met when you include the "why" behind whatever is being discussed.

The following graphic illustrates the communication loop that occurs every time information is relayed, regardless of whether it is written, verbal, or nonverbal.

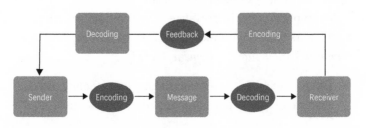

Encoding = word choice and method of delivery
Decoding = interpretation and understanding

When communication fails, we often wonder where the misinterpretation crept in. It comes down to how well an organization's communication system has been designed. Are the leaders trained in communication strategies that ensure messages are encoded in ways that make it easy for team members to decode correctly? Does the organization consistently use the same delivery method for key messages? Whether you use Post-it Notes, email, Google Chat, or Slack, be sure the method is consistent, so people know where to look. Don't use every channel available; it's too easy for something to slip through the cracks. Determine which channels are used for what, and stick to that plan.

The communication loop needs to include not only what the organization says but also how it listens. Good feedback loops confirm understanding and cut down on misinterpretations. What feedback mechanisms does your organization have?

Meetings: Key Connection Opportunities

A lot of people, leaders included, roll their eyes during meetings (or while reading about meetings in a book). One of my clients said that if he could just do away with meetings, everyone would get their work done and love their job.

The title of one of Patrick Lencioni's books, *Death by Meeting*, might give you the impression he thinks meetings are a waste of time too. On the contrary! Lencioni makes a strong case that meetings are an invaluable communication opportunity. He goes so far as to say that if you're a leader and you try to avoid meetings because you hate that part of your job, you're missing the fact that meetings *are* the job.[2]

> Meetings *are* the job.

Most leaders and owners don't know how to determine which meetings are necessary, or how to successfully organize and facilitate meetings to be productive and meaningful. But it is possible to create a meeting structure and strategy that turns those dreaded gatherings into a core method of successful communication.

If you still aren't sure about meetings, Mike Johnson, practice president of BAYADA Health Home Care, credits meetings and their system of SAY for his team's success. "We've been successful because we have built a system to support good decisions, deliberately creating a cadence of communication that allows this large team to pivot quickly and ensure that all voices are heard," he says. Referencing a particularly challenging time in the company's history, when they needed to change quickly in order to survive, Mike says, "I'm convinced that the reason we were able to change so quickly is not because we were stronger, faster, or better-looking than anybody else. We had strong communication systems in place that helped people understand what was going on, buy in, and adapt at a rapid pace."

Describing their organizational design as the foundation to their success, Mike says the company's meeting infrastructure is the highway of communication that allows for fast transport of key information and connects every member of the team across the country.

When focused on creating open dialogue, meetings allow for the entire communication loop (see the Communication Loop graphic on page 76) to be represented at one time. Unlike texts or emails, meetings offer the opportunity to share information and gather feedback immediately. Regardless of whether they are one-on-one conversations or involving a boardroom full of shareholders, they are a structured mechanism to connect the team.

So, please, get rid of any preconceived notion that meetings are the bane of your existence. They are an integral element of designing a People First organization. The key considerations for developing a systematic approach to meetings are purpose/intention, frequency, format, and attendees.

Intention: What's the Point?

The foundational purpose of meetings is alignment and connection. When done well, they can increase team engagement and allow leaders time to focus on the business. If a regular and reliable meeting structure is not part of your organizational design, you run the risk of frustrated team members who feel out of the loop, great ideas lying dormant with nowhere to surface, and people working out of alignment.

One practice administrator had a difficult time getting her physician owners to see the value of a regular staff meeting. To make time for it, they would have to shave off a few patient appointments. But she was specific about her intentions for the meeting: to improve workflow. After convincing the owners to give it a try, she was able to show the return on investment (ROI) through increased efficiencies in workflow and higher accuracy in the work. The staff began to share ideas for solutions to problems instead of complaining about them; they even wanted to implement the solutions themselves. Once everyone experienced progress, they were motivated and engaged with renewed energy. She was right: a regular staff meeting improved workflow, but it had many positive effects beyond her original intention.

Please note: if the intention for your meeting is exclusively to "tell" information, give it a reboot! Data dumps put everyone to sleep and reinforce the idea that meetings are deadly boring. Even when information exchange is coupled with increased alignment, behavior modifications, or motivating people to take action, provide the information portion in advance. Use the meeting time for a high-level overview, not regurgitation. Meetings should focus on dialogue and discussion, points of disagreement, and resolution.

Frequency: Find Your Cadence

Certain meeting formats lend themselves to specific frequency: annual all-staff gatherings, quarterly manager check-ins, weekly leadership meetings, or daily huddles. Other types of meetings are PRN—as needed for opportunities and issues that pop up unexpectedly.

You want a consistency to meeting time and frequency whenever possible. At the beginning of this chapter, Mike Johnson talked about the cadence of communication, which is really the tempo and rhythm of communication. This idea of tempo deserves careful consideration.

The schedule should not be so infrequent that the team loses its cohesion or has time to become confused. A regular time and structure help people know what to expect and gives them time to prepare, if necessary.

Once your meetings are scheduled at regular intervals, be sure to honor the time that's been set aside and actually have the meetings. Many leaders tend to cancel meetings at the last minute because "something came up" or they were "too busy." No! What message does this send to the team? How highly will they value meetings if they are constantly canceled?

Just as bad as canceling a regularly scheduled meeting is calling for a meeting at the last minute when there's a problem. Some of my smaller practices think this ad hoc method is really "all the team needs." If your MO is to call for meetings only when something goes wrong, people won't just roll their eyes—they'll actively avoid the meeting altogether. The word "meeting" will instill fear and frustration.

Format: Manage Expectations

Meetings come in many formats. The ones I've chosen to focus on here are a combination of Patrick Lencioni's work, the Entrepreneurial Operating System (EOS) model from *Traction: Get a Grip on Your Business* by Gino Wickman, and LEAN methodologies from *The Toyota Way* by Jeffrey Liker.[3]

The first three meeting formats in our discussion deserve special attention. They are often overlooked or poorly executed, though they occur at every level of the organization. Huddles involve the entire team. Monthly check-in rounds and quarterlies are between an individual team member and their leader.

Huddles

Remember the huddle muddle story from Chapter 2? The owners weren't clear on the intention of the huddle, so no one knew why they were having them. It's an easy fix.

Huddles are daily ten-minute meetings with the intention of aligning the entire team *for the day*. Keep the meeting flowing quickly and efficiently by focusing on tactical issues.

In a daily huddle, the facilitator—who is not always the organization's leader or owner—is responsible for steering the meeting. The facilitator is like a coxswain in rowing, responsible for steering the boat and coordinating the power and rhythm of the rowers. The coxswain isn't powering the meeting but simply directing it through questions that foster everyone's participation.

The following are keys to successful huddles:

- Ensure the entire team is present.

- Plan for the meeting to take no more than ten minutes.

- Align the team around activities for the day ahead.

- Review and track the challenges and successes from the previous day. Celebrate successes in the moment. If a challenge can be solved with a quick fix, resolve it in the huddle. Most challenges become items for a meeting focused on problem solving, so track it.

- Ask what the team needs to be successful today.

Notice that huddles may surface items that can't be addressed during such a short meeting format. Be grateful when that happens. It means people are speaking up.

If you think your organization is the exception to huddles, think again. Even if you have only three or four people, the purpose of huddles is alignment and connection. Taking a few minutes to gain alignment gets the team motivated in the right direction for the day.

> The purpose of huddles is alignment and connection for the day.

If you are wondering how to facilitate huddles in multiple locations, have one huddle per location. I worked in an organization where we tried a multisite huddle and it didn't work. In theory, it was good that frontline team members heard what was happening at another location, but the practicalities were that too many people were on the call sharing things that weren't relevant to other locations.

While daily alignment isn't necessarily relevant location to location, it is relevant to senior leadership. After individual office huddles, the huddle facilitators elevate their results to the next-level-up huddle. Senior leaders look for patterns and determine what needs to be elevated to a problem-solving meeting.

I love huddles because, if done well, they can prevent fires or alert you to a small fire that can be put out quickly.

Check-In Rounds

Check-in rounds are informal monthly sessions that take about fifteen minutes. Frequency and consistency are key to their success, in timing and in the questions asked. The intention of rounding is to briefly touch base with team members and hear what's happening for them.

Good fifteen-minute check-in rounds typically cover the following:

- What's going well?

- Who deserves recognition for the work they are doing? (Be sure to individually thank that person for their work. Let them know which team member recognized them.)

- Are there any tools/supplies needed to be more successful?

- What can I do to support you?

It helps for people to know the questions in advance, especially for those who like to prepare and think through their answers. Over time, new questions may be needed, so be sure to keep people up to date. For example, you may add a question to assess a new initiative.

To make the short rounds impactful, document people's responses, follow up with people who deserve recognition, address issues that have been identified, and provide the necessary tools. You'll close the feedback loop by reporting on trends and action plans at a future meeting.

Quarterlies

A new client showed me her management guidebook, which stated, "Quarterlies may be called 'quarterlies' but their frequency may vary." No! If they are quarterly, then they occur quarterly! If they are randomly planned, as needed one-on-one meetings between a manager and team member, then call them PRN Manager/Staff meetings.

I get a little fiery about quarterlies because I love them so much. Regularly planned and structured connection time is a perfect way to ensure ongoing dialogue with each team member. Leaders or managers should individually meet with everyone they directly support every three months to discuss successes, challenges, needs, and opportunities.

Even when I directly supported fifty-five team members, I made sure everyone had a quarterly without variation in their frequency. One of the reasons was that I wanted to do what I said I was going to do: meet with individuals quarterly. When I asked the team, "What's the one thing we need to continue for staff engagement?" the answer was quarterlies. Done.

Quarterlies are an opportunity for your staff to be heard, to get clear on expectations, and to understand what is required for success. They also ensure the leader is aligned with the team member's needs and that the team member is aligned with the organization's needs. They are a unique chance to demonstrate support, confirm ongoing successes, identify development opportunities, and create a strategy for growth. No matter how big or small your organization is, quarterlies are a key tool to growing your people so you can grow your business.

Here are a few sample questions and tasks for a one-hour quarterly meeting.

- What do you want to focus on today?

- What is going well?

- What is the biggest challenge you are having right now?

- Utilize the key accountabilities matrix (discussed in Chapter 8) to compare performance-to-success factors.

- Adjust their learning and development plan as needed.

- What do you need from me?

Operations Meetings

Operations meetings are to resolve tactical and practical issues identified during daily huddles, provide a feedback loop for current issues or opportunities, and discuss ways to resolve variances from metrics.

When I work with clients to discuss meeting formats, I always ask to look at their organizational chart. Owners should meet directly with the people to their immediate right: usually senior leadership. Senior leadership should meet directly with the people to their immediate right: usually the general staff. And so on. Depending on the size of your organization, you might have enough distinct service areas for an operations meeting with each team—for example, surgery center, clinical leadership, financial leadership, and so on.

Leadership operations meetings usually last between thirty and sixty minutes on a weekly basis. Staff operations meetings are typically the same length of time, one or two times a month. The length depends on the number of participants, topics, and so on.

A sample agenda might include:

- Wins for the week (or month)

- Resolving tactical issues in order of importance (larger issues move to deep dive meetings, discussed next)

- Exception reporting on key metrics

Deep Dive Meetings

Deep dives are monthly meetings with the decision makers and the people closest to the issues related to the topic of the month. Therefore, the attendees will change based on the agenda. Provide all background information in advance and then do a high-level overview to kick off the meeting and confirm agreement on the facts.

I recommend using a consistent problem-solving method (several ideas are presented in Chapter 11). Agree on your decision-making process in advance: consensus, majority rules, or 100% agreement.

Deep dives typically last between two and four hours, depending on what needs to be solved. You might think you don't have that much time, but the goal is to get ahead of challenges. Don't wait until things get so bad that you have to take days and days to resolve issues. Proactively solve problems and redesign processes to save time down the road.

Strategy Sessions

Outside of your annual strategic planning retreat, strategy sessions should be conducted quarterly to review progress and determine ways to get back on track or stay on track. Depending on the size and complexity of the strategic plan and leadership team, these sessions can be up to four hours or more. Start by confirming the mission, vision, and values. Review the overarching goals and utilize a clear system of metrics.

You've likely heard about the necessity to work not only *in* the business, but also *on* the business. Deep dives and strategy session meetings ensure you move the business forward by assessing its current state, determining the next set of goals, and resolving issues that prevent goals from being achieved.

Attendees: Who's Coming?

Who attends your meetings is just as important as their intention, frequency, and format. Depending on the particular meeting topic or intention, you may change who is included or excluded.

One of my clients told me he invited everyone on his staff to every meeting because he didn't want anyone to feel left out. While his inclusive approach is admirable, it's this kind of thinking that causes people to be bored at meetings, especially those they don't need to attend. Be thoughtful about your attendee list and considerate of what you're asking them to put aside to be at the meeting.

My client's desire to have everyone at every meeting raised questions for me about the level of trust in his organization. If every person attends every meeting, are they there to contribute or are they there to protect their position? Are they there to ensure they hear company news directly because they don't trust the middle manager? These issues can be alleviated through transparency:

- Provide meeting minutes on structure and report out process.

- Prior to ending the meeting, confirm that the meeting participants understand and can accurately relay information. Ensure participants can facilitate dialogue in their own meetings with their teams.

As I've mentioned, Mike Johnson believes that meetings are the heartbeat of the organization and tactically one of the ways you "ignite a system and the people in it." Now that is some clarity on the intention behind your meeting structure! I'm hopeful you are now asking yourself why we aren't meeting more often (and more thoughtfully). I recognize that Mike's experience leading three thousand people is different from someone who leads five, ten, or even fifty. But I have to tell you, for every successful organization I work with and every successful leader I interviewed for the book, meetings are a crucial part of the fabric of their success.

What a company says, and how it communicates internally and externally, is an integral component of People First organizational design. SAY is built on the back of organizational THINK and works in tandem with organizational DO. Understanding the composition of these essential rocks and how they are balanced is the responsibility of the organization's owners and leaders. Specific considerations for leadership SAY will be explored in the next chapter.

Self-Check: Redesign Your Meeting Structure

You've read about the power of a well-designed meeting; now let's make sure yours are as effective and efficient as possible. By reviewing your current meeting structure, intentions, and success level, you can begin to redesign your organization's communication strategy and structure. Regularly (at least annually) assessing your meeting structure ensures that your organization's needs are being addressed.

Use the grid to list every single meeting within your organization. This activity is designed to increase efficiency and effectiveness by streamlining when, why, and how you meet.

Name of Meeting			
Goals/Intention of the Meeting			
Who Attends			
Length			
Frequency			
Rate the Effectiveness of the Meeting (0–5)			

Ask each person on your team to complete this grid so you can get a handle on people's perceptions, compare notes, and identify inconsistencies or areas of confusion. Use the following questions to dig deeper if people rank the meeting less than 5.

- Was the meeting the right length of time? Too long? Too short?

- Was the intent of the meeting effectively communicated and clear to those in the room?

- Were the right people (and only the right people) in attendance?

- Were the meeting leaders prepared?

- Would you recommend this meeting to others? What is your reason for the yes or no answer?

Please understand: the transition to a new meeting structure won't go perfectly at first. Just like any other change, facilitating and participating in meetings requires practice and coaching. Initially, you may experience silence or people going off topic. They may not realize that the new structure requires they come prepared for a dialogue, or that they are encouraged to participate instead of sitting quietly listening. When the appropriate meeting structure has been determined, stick with it because it will get better with practice and time.

6

The SAY Leadership Factor

S AY IS SMALL but mighty. Even if you're doing all the right things, words can add or subtract from those efforts. They set the tone for the organization. SAY is the rock that builds trust by reinforcing the intentions behind your actions. Without SAY, DO won't stand as tall, and THINK won't be articulated.

As a leader, your communication impacts the team's response. Leadership SAY isn't designed to give you a script for how to have difficult conversations or facilitate meetings. It's designed to get you to THINK about what you SAY, and ensure that your words reflect your mindset and intentions.

This chapter explores the fundamentals of leadership SAY that apply to every aspect of leadership communication. Understanding these core aspects will allow you to successfully express yourself in any type of interaction.

Three Little Words

In 2011, while I was a participant in the LAMP Institute for Leadership program, the facilitator explained something that profoundly changed my life. Talking about his own paradigm shift with language, he explained that he had moved from thinking of the people who worked for his company as "employees" to thinking of them as the "people I support." With those words, his view of his role as a leader was transformed. Because his language reinforced that his primary role was to support others, he acted in new ways that demonstrated that support.

After hearing this story, I went home and tried out those three little words myself. The mindset shift was profound. Language shaped my behavior. I began to focus on creating a cohesive team culture and supporting people's professional development.

Three additional little words also served to transform my thinking: "Help me understand." In the past, if something went wrong or someone had a different opinion, I responded with, "Why did that happen?" or "Why did you do that?" Those words matched my mindset, which was investigative and judgmental. But I didn't want to be a judge; I wanted to be supportive. "Help me understand" was a more effective set of words, and they matched my new mindset of curiosity. They are a reminder that every situation offers an opportunity to learn something new, and they communicate to the person I'm interacting with that I care where they're coming from.

Through experiencing the impact of language on my own behaviors, I began to pay much closer attention to the power of words and how they set the tone for every conversation. Consider the common phrases, "I'm so busy" or "Work is crazy." In an *Inc.* magazine article, "3 Phrases Confident Leaders Use Every Day," Julia Bonner says that replacing those phrases with, "I'm really focused on this part of work" shifts the implication that you're dealing with more than you can handle to one of calm and control. They indicate that you are in the driver's seat, which changes how you think about what's on your plate.[1]

Reflect on the common phrases that are peppered throughout your vernacular. What mental image do they evoke? How do your words impact your actions and your mindset?

The Brain Game

Have you ever been in a meeting or conversation and had an immediate, almost physical reaction to what's being said? Even before you consciously recognize the emotion associated with the words, your brain has reacted to them.

Our responses are neurologically hardwired, which is why leaders should be aware of their ability to influence behaviors through word choice. Certain words trigger a person to either accept or reject concepts or ideas that are presented to them. Acceptance or rejection relate back to the Communication Loop discussed in Chapter 5, when we wonder how intentions are misinterpreted. The person speaking encodes their intentions through word choice, either by accident or design. Leaders need to ensure their messages are encoded in such a way that the recipient is able to decode those messages as intended.

A 2016 white paper titled "Words That Don't Work" revealed that "[c]ertain words can cause a sudden and negative response in conversation."[2] Through EEG brain scans, TTI Success Insights observed gamma brain activity in the frontal cortex and classified the activity as depicting acceptance, avoidance, or neutral symmetry.

In this study, Dr. Ron Bonnstetter and Bill J. Bonnstetter determined what words work (depict acceptance) and what words don't work (depict avoidance) for each of the four DISC behavioral styles (Dominance, Influence, Steadiness, and Conscientiousness) developed by psychologist William Moulton Marston. This same process has been applied to words and their ability to motivate or demotivate a person based on their individual driving forces.

I've seen this research validated with client after client. During our team dynamics session, I walk through a variety of words and ask for their reactions to assess their behavioral style. Many times, I don't even need to ask because their face reveals their feelings.

One of my clients led a team of twenty-four people. For reasons unknown to him, they couldn't seem to move their work forward. Upon assessing their individual natural behavioral tendencies and driving forces, the problem became crystal clear. (We'll talk about intrinsic motivators in greater detail in Chapter 8.) About half of the team was motivated by new ideas and out-of-the-box thinking and the other half was motivated by traditional approaches and proven methods. The situation reminded me of Susan and Bob from Chapter 2. Susan was motivated by change; Bob was motivated by consistency.

So, what happened with my client's team? The structured folks got frustrated every time their leader said, "Let's try something new." Much like Bob, their brains decoded that message as, "Let's get rid of what has worked before and try something untested/unproven." Of course, they shut down right away and were no longer motivated by the activity.

On the flipside, the people who were motivated by new ideas got frustrated when their leader said, "This is the way we've always done it." And much like Susan, their brains decoded the message as, "We don't support change and growth." They, too, shut down.

The good news is that there is a way to find the middle ground and get this team aligned. By using language that tickles the neurons of both groups, you will elicit more uniform responses. For example, "We want to build on our proven methods by adding in some new elements" uses words that motivate everyone toward the same goal, even though they are hardwired to achieve the goal in different ways. Leaders must make a concerted effort to know their audience so they can tailor their messages appropriately.

Compassionate Candor

In addition to knowing your audience, you also have to know yourself and how you respond to information. For outgoing and people-oriented people like me, social rejection is a common fear. I often found myself sugar-coating or avoiding productive conflict because I wanted people to like me. Some people want things to be stable and don't want to rock the boat. Other people are competitive and decisive. They fear someone will take advantage of them. So, they jump eagerly into conflict conversations with little regard for the other person.

As leaders and owners, we've got to balance our own personal communication delivery style with other people's style of receiving. Many struggle with either being really nice but unclear or rude and crystal clear.

I spent years trying to find the right way to communicate my expectations in a caring but direct manner. One of my clients dubbed my communication style "compassionate candor"—two words I happen to love. Rooted in the People First mindset, compassionate candor acknowledges the other person's value and allows for a frank discussion to resolve whatever issues are present.

When I adopted the People First mindset, I vowed to "treat every problem as a chance to build a relationship." In fact, that early vow became my motto and the foundation of my communication style. Just like any skill, compassionate candor can be developed over time and with a little practice.

Listen First

Compassionate candor is demonstrated by listening fully, not just hearing what you want to hear. Listening shows you are committed to the other person's point of view. It puts you in a mindset of compassion and curiosity and ensures you have the information you need to move forward. The intention is to understand, not to confirm what you already believe to be true.

A recent study in the *Journal of General Internal Medicine* examined the extent to which physicians elicit patient concerns and then listen to the responses. The study found that physicians:

- Used questions to elicit the patient's agenda 36% of the time
- Waited approximately eleven seconds before interrupting the patient
- Interrupted to ask a close-ended yes or no question 60% of the time

Couple this data with multiple studies that show men interrupt women 33% more often than they interrupt other men, and you'll see we have a real challenge when it comes to listening first.[3]

That said, not all listening is created equal. The Co-Active Coaching Model defines Three Levels of Listening.[4] Level 1 listening is when you hear someone else's story and relate it to your own experience. For example, someone tells you about their vacation and you automatically start thinking about your vacation. You imagine their vacation as it relates to you, instead of focusing on what it meant to them.

In Level 1 listening, you might find yourself saying something like, "You think Sanibel is nice. Let me tell you about when I went to Hawaii…" I used to be guilty of Level 1 listening all the time because I thought I was "relating" to the other person by sharing my own experience. In reality, I was just relating their experience to my own without truly listening to how they experienced it or what they thought or felt about it.

In Level 2 listening, you're so focused on the other person that your thoughts quiet and you don't notice anything beyond what they are saying. Your awareness and attention is 100% attuned to them, to the degree that you have let go of your own agenda and inner voice. Level 2 listening allows for deep connection because you're listening for the nuances of the other person's story.

And finally, there is Level 3 listening, which is when you fully hear the other person while also tapping into your intuition. Your intuition is the gut feeling that allows you to connect. In Level 3, your inner voice is active but not in the context of comparing the person's experience to your own or letting your mind drift away from the conversation. You are truly listening.

The Three Levels of Listening are different from active listening, which encompasses physical movements such as head nodding, leaning in, and mirroring the speaker's body language. While these cues can help convey that you're listening, they don't ensure you truly hear what the other person is saying.

Listening sessions do not need to be long to be impactful. In fact, a ten-minute conversation at Level 2 or 3 is much more effective than thirty minutes at Level 1. Make the most of your time, and other people's time too, by making an effort to listen first. When people feel heard, they also feel valued. Feeling valued leads to a deeper connection.

Powerful Questions

Asking powerful questions is another component of developing compassionate candor. Powerful questions help you get to the core of the matter quickly and effectively.

Just like the Three Levels of Listening, not all questions are created equal. Do your questions build connection, drive change, and improve outcomes? Often, people use questions with the intention of leading the discussion in a certain direction. The questions they pose are usually focused on having their own needs met rather than the needs of the other person. An open and curious mind is required for powerful questions to work.

Powerful questions are typically brief, no more than seven words. Don't attempt to couch a question in a lot of words or lead with a long preamble. Those tactics only cloud the question's clarity and impede understanding. They should be simple, direct, and open-ended, meaning you're looking for more than a yes or no answer. Critically, they don't insert a desired or suspected answer, and they don't take an accusatory tone.

Take a look at some typical questions versus powerful ones. How does each of these questions make you feel when you read them? Do you feel defensive or empowered?

Typical Questions	Powerful Questions
In addition to more training, what do you think will help you?	What will help you be successful?
The program really went well. Why did you switch the order of the onboarding process?	How do you think the program went? What do you think made it successful?
What do you think about changing the process to X?	What do you think we should do?
This clearly didn't work, so what are you going to do differently next time?	What could we do differently next time?
Reliability is so important. So, what are you going to do to make sure we have reliable results all the time?	How can we consistently re-create these results?
Why isn't the team doing a good job, and what are you going to do about it?	What ideas do you have to improve performance?

The questions on the right invite reflection and an exploration of the possibilities. Unlike the questions on the left, they don't specify the direction in which you want the response to go.

Let's talk about one little word that so many questions begin with: "why." On a conscious level, we know "why" is about curiosity. Think about how many times children ask, "Why?" They're simply looking for answers in the big wide world. And it sounds innocent enough, but somehow, "why" sounds different when it comes from your boss. Even if the question is posed in a neutral voice with neutral body language, what's the first thing you think when your boss asks, "Why?" You think, "Oh boy, what did I do wrong?" "Why" puts people on the defensive, which is the last thing you want people to feel if your goal is open communication based in compassionate candor.

Asking powerful questions is about understanding, on a conceptual level, what types of inquiries will foster an open and honest dialogue. These types of conversations promote an environment of critical thinking and engagement.

Throughout this book, you've read about coaching—the mindset of a coach and the benefits of coaching for you and your team. One of the best books on coaching is by Michael Bungay Stanier. The title, *The Coaching Habit: Say Less, Ask More & Change the Way You Lead Forever*, says it all. Powerful questions are one of the key skills to becoming not only a coach but a better leader.[5]

Feedback and Feedforward

Compassionate candor can be further explored in the context of feedback and feedforward. The minute I say the word "feedback," where does your mind go? "Feedback" implies looking backward, at the past, to examine what did or didn't go well. Let's be honest, any sentence that begins with, "I want to give you some feedback" immediately causes you to assume a negative discussion is forthcoming. And you're usually right.

Surveys reveal that more than one-third of managers feel uncomfortable about having to give feedback, in part because most people associate it with criticism.[6] Yet, we all crave information about our performance, and we all want to get better and grow.

Compassionate candor in SAY leadership flips the concept of feedback into "feedforward." In his article "10 Surefire Reasons to Try Feedforward!," Marshall Goldsmith makes an excellent case to ditch traditional feedback. "Feedforward tends to be much faster and more efficient than feedback... An excellent technique for giving ideas to successful people is to say, 'Here are four ideas for the future. Please accept these in the positive spirit that they are given.'"[7]

Goldsmith's example does two important things: first, it states the intention, and second, it focuses on improvement over incrimination. Feedforward acknowledges that something needs to change but implies the person can and will make progress. It is best offered when the situation is fresh, before too much time has passed.

By asking three powerful questions, you can combine feedback and feedforward in an effective and efficient manner.

1. **WHAT IS THE GOAL?** This allows the person to clarify the goal and confirm you are on the same page.

2. **HOW ARE YOU PROGRESSING TOWARD THE GOAL?** This gives the person an opportunity to provide feedback on themselves, which opens the door for a brief discussion about the past.

3. **WHAT SHOULD YOU DO NEXT?** This is about future actions toward the goal. Now, the discussion moves into feedforward, focusing on actions the person can take for success. Once this portion is complete, recap the plan, outcomes expected, and timelines.

I like to add one more question to almost every conversation I have with someone. "What else do you need from me?" reinforces your intention to provide support.

"What else do you need from me?"

As much as I like the idea of feedforward versus feedback, not all feedback is bad. In fact, positive feedback is an essential part of leadership SAY, and it's not given out often enough or correctly. Recognition makes people feel good. It makes them want to stay with the company and continue to do good work. Surveys show that when managers focus on people's strengths and successes, team members are fully engaged in their work.[8] Some benefits of positive feedback include:

- Recognizing work that supports the mission, vision, and values of the organization

- Reinforcing good behavior you want to see replicated

- Showing you value the individual's contributions

There are several ways to ensure that positive feedback is effective and long-lasting. Be specific. It's not enough to casually say, "Good job" when passing someone in the hallway. Take the time to go find the person, identify what they did well, and articulate the impact their work has on the organization—for example, "Hey, John, great job on calming down that frustrated patient. You were able to prevent a problem from escalating and upsetting the rest of the patients in the waiting room."

Being specific also applies to showing appreciation. While a generic "Thank you" is a step in the right direction, the more specific you are about why you're thanking someone, the more likely they are to repeat the behavior. You could say, for example, "Thank you for cleaning up the front desk area. You do such a great job with it, and it encourages everyone to keep it clean longer." Yes, a clean area is part of the job, but this specific thank-you explains why doing their job well impacts the whole team. Expressing gratitude in a meaningful way is just a small part of a leader's toolkit for SAY.

There are countless opportunities throughout the day to influence the team with words. The entire team is paying attention to what you SAY, as well as how, when, and where it is said. The systems of SAY weave the fabric of your organizational culture. As the leader, bring your full awareness and attention to this central rock upon which DO is balanced.

Self-Check: You Said What?

You read about how three little words changed my thoughts and behaviors. Words truly do matter, yet we so often don't even realize the words or phrases we are using over and over again.

Over the next few days, jot down words that you say often. Ask colleagues and trusted peers what your "catchphrases" are. Also pay attention to your overall communication style.

Self-check questions:

1. What words and phrases do you regularly use?

2. Do they align with your People First mindset and intentions?

3. What could you replace them with to better reflect People First?

4. How often do you start talking before the other person is finished?

5. Can you add a pause before jumping into a conversation?

6. Do your comments add to the current point or are you shifting focus?

7. Do your questions tend to include the answer you've already determined to be true?

THREE

DO

7

Align and Inspire: The People First Approach to Onboarding and Orientation

I N CHAPTER 4, I introduced you to my turning point down the People First path—the nomenclature for the employee lifecycle:

- Attract and Select (versus Recruit and Hire)

- Align and Inspire (versus Onboard and Orient)

- Engage and Empower (versus Retain)

Building on that nomenclature, the next three chapters will explore the DO component of each phase. We begin our discussion with Align and Inspire because attracting and selecting candidates is the successful by-product of aligning, inspiring, engaging, and empowering the people who are *already on your team*. Those activities are the core functions of an organization's DO.

Many practices miss a critical opportunity to create a real and meaningful connection between a new hire and the organization during the onboarding and orientation phases. Largely, the opportunity is missed because the focus is on checklists and paperwork instead of aligning the person to the organization. People First organizational design flips the traditional approach on its head and reimagines onboarding for maximum engagement from the get-go.

Day One: Harness the Excitement

Think about how you felt the last time you started a new job. You were probably hopeful, nervous, eager, and excited about what lay ahead. I imagine those feelings were even stronger if you were attracted to the company by its reputation.

One of my good friends experienced those first-day jitters when she landed her dream job, working for an organization she'd had her eye on for a long time. For the first time in her career, she was nervous. She wanted to knock it out of the park, and make a good impression on the team.

On her first day, she was riding high on excitement because her new organization viewed onboarding as a time to align and inspire. She took that as a very good sign. The emphasis on day one was on building her connection to the team. They also spent time making sure she understood the organization's big-picture goals as well as how her role contributed to those goals. She told me that at the end of her first day, she was all in.

By focusing on alignment and inspiration, the organization was able to turn my friend's excitement and nervousness into energy and momentum for the work. She was fully invested in the organizational goals. Dedicated to her responsibilities, she brought all of her skills and energy to work, increased her efforts, and deeply committed to the organization's success.

I recall an "orientation" experience that was the exact opposite of my friend's. I was stationed at a tiny desk, like the kind they have in elementary school, and instructed to read through a lengthy policy and procedure manual. Snore!

Starting a new job shouldn't be about sitting at a desk, reading a manual, and being tested on its contents. Yet, Human Capital Institute research shows that "37% of formal onboarding programs focus on processes and paperwork."[1] While this data is not specific to healthcare, the statistic is certainly applicable to the industry.

To move beyond the checklist, change your perspective on the goals and functions of onboarding by adapting a People First orientation program. Shift your thinking from "getting them up and running quickly" to creating a deep connection between the new person's role and the organizational goals. This not only creates momentum during the learning phase; it increases the likelihood the person will stick around and bring their A game to work every day. Ultimately, people want to feel they are in the right place, doing work that matters. How can you ensure you tap into people's inherent desire to belong and contribute?

Are You Onboarding or Boring?

The following chart compares traditional orientation and onboarding design to the best-practice People First design. Notice the subtle but critical differences between the two columns.

Traditional Approach	People First Approach
Who, What, When, Where, How	Why (Mission, Vision, Values) Who, What, When, Where, How
Standardized checklist	Individualized plan
Preceptor	Coach
Introduction to the team	Connection to the team
Monitoring their performance	Monitoring your performance

In the pages ahead, I'll break down each of these five differences between aligning and inspiring versus onboarding and orienting.

Who, What, When, Where, and How. Oh Yeah, and Why.

Every orientation program includes the "who, what, when, where, and how" elements of a job. The difference in the People First orientation plan is that these considerations aren't the only priority, or even the first things to be addressed.

Instead, People First starts with the organization's mission and purpose, *why* the role exists, and *why* the new hire has been selected for it. By focusing on these key topics first, a new hire gains a deeper understanding of how their work is to be done and the importance of it.

Then—as they learn the who, what, when, where, and how—they can see how each task associated with their position connects to the larger organizational design. People are given the opportunity to recognize they are part of an ecosystem that thrives when all of the parts work together. That recognition creates engagement right out of the gate.

Fundamentally, people need purpose in their work lives. They seek inspiration, and an onboarding program needs to spark that inspiration. In healthcare, we have a simplistic view about why people do they work they do. The assumption is that people go into patient care to "help people," but there's more to it than that. Plus, there are many roles within a healthcare organization that don't have a solid line to the patients: you can't assume that "helping people" is a driver for them.

> People need purpose in their work lives.

So, how do you align an individual's purpose and values with the organization's? A former colleague created an excellent activity to do just that during the company's orientation welcome session. She asked the participants to create an imaginary company they owned. (Don't ask me why, but they always came up with a flower shop or a car wash.)

Next, she asked the group to explain how they would ensure customer satisfaction, high quality service and products, a balanced budget, and employee engagement. Then, they brought those activities back to the work of their own practice. They developed the strategies for customer satisfaction in their specific roles. The process was repeated for their role's impact on the financial bottom line, patient safety, and other important organizational initiatives.

Before wrapping up the session, each new team member reviewed a tool created by people who were already working in their role. The tool outlined success factors, organizational values, and desired behaviors. Real-life examples and guidelines moved alignment from an idea to action.

When I ask people how their role contributes to the organization's mission, I want them to go deeper than a general response such as, "I'm a physician assistant, so I help people." I want them to explore their responsibilities and tasks and how they relate to the mission statement's different components.

For example, a portion of my former organization WellSpan Health's mission statement referred to "lifelong wellness." Imagine how those words might impact a physician assistant who is aligned with lifelong wellness when she conducts a physical for a Department of Transportation truck driver from out of state. The PA may see that truck driver only once, but catching a dangerously high blood pressure can save his life. She keeps that focus and brings that "why" with her to every blood pressure reading she takes.

I'm reminded of an organization I worked with where the billing department was frustrated because the schedulers "weren't doing their job," which made it difficult for the billers to do theirs. When we examined the problem, it turned out the schedulers weren't checking one important box on the intake form. Though they had been trained to check the box, they weren't doing it. When I interviewed the schedulers, the box wasn't even on their radar; they thought it was redundant from another part of the form. Once billing explained to scheduling why that box made a difference in their work, the schedulers started to check the box and workflow improved dramatically. This simple example demonstrates that if people don't understand the "why" behind their work, they may take shortcuts without being aware of the downstream effects.

Individualized Plans for True Mastery

We often think of productivity as the ability to complete a task. True productivity is the ability to function independently: to complete tasks automatically, quickly, and without error. If someone needs clarification on the task, has to search several places to find the right equipment, or pauses to review the procedure manual, then they aren't fully productive. Research suggests that employees do not reach full productivity until eight months to two years after they are hired.[2]

Psychologist Noel Burch of Gordon Training International created a learning model with four stages in the 1970s. The final stage of his model is called "unconsciously competent." Also described as "true mastery," it is the ability to do the job seamlessly and singularly. Who doesn't want an organization staffed by fully productive true masters who are unconsciously competent and inspired to do their personal best every day?

Getting to true mastery requires an individualized learning and development plan for each person. Individualized plans provide a clear roadmap that encompasses the baseline job requirements, assesses what skills the person already possesses, and identifies the gaps that need development. This tailored approach is effective and efficient because it doesn't waste time on developing skills the person already has; instead, it focuses on skills that need improvement.

Coaches versus Preceptors

Many healthcare practices use job trainers referred to as "preceptors." According to Dictionary.com, a preceptor is an instructor, teacher, or tutor.[3] You see where I'm going with this. The nomenclature of "preceptor" doesn't fit in with a People First approach because a preceptor's only DO is to instruct. They ensure new hires know where everything is and what time they start the day, and they monitor all of the tasks—large and small—that are completed during a shift. Preceptors are important in healthcare, but they don't address all of a new hire's needs during onboarding.

While we've already covered the benefits of coaching versus teaching, let's look at the coach's role during the initial onboarding period. A coach meets with the new team member at least weekly for a sit-down discussion to review progress, challenges, and opportunities for the coming week. The coach listens to how the person is feeling about their experience so adjustments can be made.

If the coach is not also the new hire's supervisor or manager, then the supervisor also needs to plan regular check-in meetings. A supervisory check-in should be a high-level discussion about what is going well, who needs to be recognized for helping, and what the organization can do better to improve the experience.

I've Got This: Building Self-Reliance

Remember the first time you went to work in a new setting, different from the one you trained in? Perhaps you shifted specialties or went from being a treating clinician to a business owner.

During such transitions, it's natural to experience the unsettling feeling that you don't know everything you need to know. Likely, you wanted to succeed at whatever you were doing, so you sought help from others. Maybe you felt tentative about the work and not fully confident in your skills. If, by some point, you don't gain a level of confidence, you are more prone to lose engagement in the work, become frustrated, and potentially start to feel burnout.

To feel fully engaged, people need to have a sense of self-efficacy or confidence in their ability to perform the work.

They've got to be able to say, "I've got this." That assurance is derived from a feeling of self-reliance and the idea that they can do things for themselves.

While self-reliance starts with knowledge, practice, and skill development, it is the application of knowledge and critical thinking in a variety of situations that builds a person's confidence and sense of self-reliance. This type of development doesn't require an instructor; it requires a coach who asks powerful questions and provides feedforward. Coaching is a People First best practice because it builds self-reliance by taking the person's specific challenges and/or assets into consideration.

Connection to the Team

So much of traveling the People First path is about connection, and it's a core aspect of the aligning and inspiring process. Most organizations walk a new person around and introduce them to everyone. This step is not a connection-building experience for new team members; it serves only to put names with faces. Real connection is about getting to know each other and building trust.

If your organization is small, with between two and ten people, team connection may happen organically. But the larger an organization, the harder it is for a new person to figure out whom to connect with and how to best collaborate. It's partly the organization's responsibility to foster team connectivity and create opportunities for new people to get to know the rest of the team.

It has always irked me that companies throw going away parties when someone leaves. We should celebrate when someone joins the team instead, and shift those parties from endings to beginnings. Team connection is a huge component of keeping people engaged and empowered, so you will find much more on this key topic in Chapter 8.

Monitoring *Your* Performance

While we need to monitor a new person's performance, the People First approach includes monitoring the organization's performance too. Your organizational design must include a feedback loop for the orientation program to uncover opportunities to improve. Consider quantitative data such as turnover in the first year, or employee errors and injury rates in the first two years.

Don't forget to include qualitative data collected through regularly scheduled check-ins. Just as with any meeting, I've had clients initially balk at the time investment, but once they implemented consistent, structured check-ins, they discovered time is actually saved in the overall learning curve for the new team member. The core purpose of this activity is to monitor organizational performance *in addition to* individual performance. What are you doing to improve your orientation and onboarding processes?

Play the Long Game

I recently surveyed 250 organizations to assess how long their onboarding and orientation programs are. Over 50% said one to two weeks. A training time of this length means you can focus only on instructing a new hire on what processes to follow, and then monitor their performance for success or failure. Competency assessment is important, but I encourage you to think beyond the basics.

Spooner Physical Therapy recognizes that onboarding must go deeper. Their program is designed with monthly milestones for the first twelve months, and periodically thereafter depending on the position. For example, the process is typically two years for a director-level position. Yes, two years! Founded in 1990, Spooner determined that their longevity hinges on their team members' longevity. Thus, their onboarding program focuses on their core purpose and values, along with the treatment philosophy, which anchors the entire team (including new hires) to those values and ensures they drive the focus of the organization.

Think beyond the basics.

Similarly, The Hello Foundation's orientation program is stretched out over the course of a year. The founder and CEO, Sharon Soliday, explained that, with more than ninety employees, they have a dedicated team member whose entire job is to provide orientation. Consequently, The Hello Foundation has single-digit turnover. When people leave, it's usually due to personal life changes such as moving or having a baby, and the owner celebrates those departures.

Don't panic: new hires at both of these organizations can safely and independently do their jobs much before one or two years there; it's mastery that takes that long. These companies recognize that protecting the team's longevity requires more than a two-week training program. They both boast employee tenures in the ten- and twenty-year range instead of the 2.8 yearly average in healthcare.[4]

Beyond these two examples, a large-scale survey by Glassdoor revealed that "[o]rganizations with a strong onboarding process improve new hire retention by 82% and productivity by over 70%."[5] Playing the long game during orientation is

Protecting the team's longevity requires more than a two-week training program.

part of what generates these statistics and the success or failure of the remaining stages in the employee lifecycle.

The People First path has clear organizational DOs when it comes to ensuring full productivity by aligning and inspiring new team members. While Align and Inspire is designed to replace onboarding and orientation, the principles I've shared here can be applied to the next phase of the lifecycle, Engage and Empower, as well.

Self-Check: Align and Inspire

Before we move on, ask yourself what message your onboarding conveys. Does it say, "I need you to get to patients as quickly as possible, so check this list and get going!" Or does it say, "We want to make sure you have everything you need to succeed here!" Think about how the person will feel after their first day with your organization given the two different approaches. In addition to asking your managers and team members, be sure to ask your most recent hires for their input.

1. Have you provided training for your coaches so they can foster self-reliance in the new team member?

2. Have you customized a coaching plan based on your new hire's strengths and the gaps identified during selection?

3. Have you created opportunities for connection beyond just name and face recognition?

4. Can the entire team speak to the mission, vision, and values of the company as well as how their role contributes to each?

5. Do you have regularly scheduled check-ins with the new team member? Start with weekly, then do monthly, before moving to the quarterly and annual meeting structure.

6. Do you have a feedback tool for new team members to provide input on the organization's success with the orientation process?

8

Engage and Empower: The People First Approach to Retention

WHILE PEOPLE FIRST onboarding is an opportunity to build alignment and inspiration, team member longevity is the result of an environment in which people are engaged and empowered. In a traditional model, this concept is called "retention." I defined these in Chapter 4, but I offer a refresher here on the nuances among retain, engage, and empower:

1. RETAIN: keep possession of; keep in one's service by paying

2. ENGAGE: having full attention, being fully occupied, focused, and involved

3. EMPOWER: to give someone the official authority, or the freedom or confidence to do something

Would you rather your staff feel retained or engaged? Exactly! So, drop the word "retain" from your vocabulary right now.

Many of you already know about the concept of engagement. It may even be a focus area in your practice. I've added empowerment to this stage because when your people are self-reliant, confident, and autonomous, you'll have more time and freedom to grow your business.

The engagement and empowerment cairn of organizational design has four basic components: 1) Tools to do the job, 2) Connection to the team, 3) Support and Accountability, and 4) Growth and Development. We'll examine each of these elements in detail and explore what to DO as you design (or redesign) your organization in accordance with the People First approach.

Growth & Development

Support & Accountability

Connection to the Team

Tools to Do the Job

Tools to Do the Job

Every team member must have the tools they need to do their job. Essentially, this is the who, what, when, where, and how of the job, which we discussed in the previous chapter. People need to know how to use the equipment safely, what the procedures are for certain tasks, and where to get the supplies they need. Because, yes, engagement is tied to the literal tools of the job.

For example, the electronic health record is the most frequently used tool in healthcare. It also leads to the most frustration. Devote time to teaching people how to use this tool correctly. The training will benefit new hires and the existing staff. Knowing how to use the basic tools of the job fosters engagement and self-reliance.

I encouraged one of my clients to add a question about the tools of the job to rounding check-ins and he was shocked by what he discovered. Turns out, there weren't enough computer stations for recently hired staff, and a key piece of equipment was broken. For this organization, the equipment issue became a watershed moment. It put the organization's severe communication issues and the impact on the business into full focus.

Key Accountabilities Matrix

An incredibly helpful tool for engagement is a key accountabilities matrix for each role. Key accountabilities provide a higher level of clarity on expectations than job descriptions, and it's much easier to be successful when you fully understand what is expected.

Key accountabilities focus on outcomes instead of providing a laundry list of tasks. They require the organization to clearly articulate which accountability is the highest priority and how much time it should take to successfully complete each area of accountability. Finally, key accountability matrices include success factors that describe expected outcomes.

Key Accountability	Priority	% of Time	Success Factors

Facility Operations Management
 	
• Employee Schedule (clinical and non-clinical staff). Employee functions including schedules
 	
  ~ Coordinate and manage PTO, CEU, and other schedule requests for your location
 	
  ~ Coordinate cross-collaboration with other locations
	3	50%	• All areas fully staffed for given caseloads
			
			• Evaluations are scheduled within guidelines
			
			• Minimal gaps in clinic schedule to ensure units/ hour metrics met (outpatient, LTC productivity, and school caseload)
			
			• Waiting list < 5 days

Please note: Key accountabilities aren't one-size-fits-all. While many of the practices I work with have the same jobs, each organization's key accountabilities will look different according to their unique mission and values.

The success factors in the far-right column are critical for performance improvement. *Helping People Win at Work: A Business Philosophy Called "Don't Mark My Paper, Help Me Get an A,"* by Ken Blanchard and Garry Ridge (CEO of WD-40), explains how. Based on WD-40's own success in nearly doubling profit growth and increasing employee satisfaction to over 93%, the book explores a model of partnering with team members to build personal success.[1] Putting the employee in the driver's seat empowers them to make choices and know what they are measured on and what it takes to excel in the organization.

Don't create key accountabilities in a vacuum. Enlist your best and brightest—people who are already performing well in the role—to be part of creating the matrix. Inviting current team members to share good, better, and best practices ensures that key aspects are captured and clearly explained.

Key accountability planning sessions can be a powerful engagement tool too. Often, they lead to interesting discussions beyond the specific role being addressed. You might discover there are competing priorities that need to be resolved. I facilitated a planning session that led to a deeper conversation about the difference between marketing and community relations, an important distinction for the organization's growth plans.

One owner I worked with was excited about the process because he just "couldn't get people to do what needed to be done" for a certain position. Building out the key accountabilities revealed that each person in the room had a different view of the position's function. How can people meet expectations if they can't agree on what those expectations are?

Another client was shocked to discover that the reason people weren't getting the work done was that there simply wasn't enough time in the day. When they looked at the percent of time needed for certain activities, they realized it added up to well over 100%. And another client identified that managers were spending too much time on tasks that could be taken care of by someone in a lower salary bracket. He hired an administrative assistant, which freed up the managers to focus on higher-level work.

These examples illustrate not only the necessity for individualized key accountability matrices, but also the value of the planning process. If you're not already using this effective tool, get started immediately because the impacts are profound.

Connection to the Team

The idea of building connection is woven into every section of this book. Mission statements, meetings, onboarding, coaching, and team goals are all ways to build connection.

That said, let's compare building connection to traditional team building. I love the idea of some of the more extreme team-building activities I've come across, like rope courses or skydiving. But are those types of off-site initiatives really the key to team building? Sure, they create a shared experience, but an escape room focuses people on a common goal only for a few hours. Unless a facilitator helps explore parallels at work, it doesn't necessarily unite them around a common work goal or build lasting connection.

If you want the team to unite around a common work goal, give them a problem to solve or process to fix. Solving real issues at work builds bonds that last. It also connects people to the organization because they know how integral they are to its success.

Ask your team how they want to connect and let them get creative. Incorporate ways for team members to share gratitude for each other. Orchestrate fun activities that give people an opportunity to learn more about each other. A few ideas include fun-fact bingo, a scavenger hunt, sharing baby pictures, or building a team crest.

A feeling of connection is also a feeling of belonging. When everyone knows why they're doing what they're doing and feels confident in how their work supports another person, their sense of belonging increases. Knowing that someone trusts and relies on their work feeds into that connection. Ensure time for team members to share their expertise with each other. Gather feedback on ideas for improvement, share the strategic plan, and help people see their role in achieving it.

I worked with one organization whose managers said, "Our team doesn't need to connect regularly. We're a small group, and I see everyone all the time." Connection is not about saying hi across the workstation or passing someone in the hallway. It's about getting to know people on a personal level and understanding what makes them tick.

Think about your friends versus your acquaintances. You may know people from yoga class or pickup basketball, but are they your true friends, the people you rely on? Unless you connect beyond a shared activity or common space, they probably aren't the people you're closest to. Friends know about what's important in your life, your goals and challenges, and they try to help you meet them. In the workplace, meetings are the structures that allow people to share goals and challenges and seek help from their team.

Connected teams are anchored to the organization's core values, the treatment philosophy, and the mission. They are bound by shared successes and quality outcomes. Because there is clarity on each person's accountability, team members recognize each other's contribution, even when it's different from their own.

The People First approach reframes team-building activities: from taking place once a quarter to daily; from the annual party to high-impact huddles; from "Jersey Fridays" to real demonstrations of solidarity, such as helping a colleague out during challenging times. Team connectivity is increased when the opportunity to gather is presented more frequently and has value beyond just having a few laughs. Can you appreciate the value of meetings as a way to build connection?

Support and Accountability

I find it much easier to go about my day when I know somebody's got my back. I like the feeling that someone is there to help me if I get stuck or fall behind. I want someone to celebrate with when good things happen. Given how many of our waking hours we spend at work, that "someone" needs to include your colleagues and leaders.

For a team to feel supported, they need to see that everyone is being held accountable in a just and equitable way. Roger Connors and Tom Smith's book, *How Did That Happen?*, examines accountability in a "positive and principled way." The authors explain that holding people accountable requires more than a cursory or infrequent evaluation to assess if people did what was expected of them. Instead, they lay out a four-step process that places ownership on the leaders first and then on the individual:

1. Form expectations

2. Communicate expectations

3. Align expectations

4. Inspect expectations[2]

The People First approach is very much in alignment with Connors and Smith's perspective. When well crafted, the key accountabilities matrix is an excellent tool to create and communicate expectations, and various meetings provide the opportunity to align and inspect expectations.

Trust and Autonomy

Sharon Soliday, founder and CEO of The Hello Foundation, describes the People First path as quid pro quo. She trusts people will get their work done because they are professionals. In turn, her team trusts her to put people first.

Many of my clients find trust and autonomy very difficult at first. Yet, every leader interviewed for this book mentioned those two words at least once during our conversation.

Developing trust and autonomy ties to organizational design. How strong are your communication systems? Do people understand how they add value to the organization? Are they given the tools to succeed? Autonomy is the result of people knowing what they need to do and when. Once those issues are addressed, my clients often discover that their lack of trust was actually due to the systems, not the people.

Growth and Development

Public opinion research company The Harris Poll reported that lack of career growth is the second biggest reason people quit their jobs.[3] As discussed, creating a key accountabilities matrix for each person's role is a critical growth tool. Understanding people's intrinsic motivators and providing them with organizational structures for growth through a career rock wall and annual reviews will only enhance each individual's likelihood of reaching their goals. We'll examine each of those three tools next.

Intrinsic Motivators:
Know Your People to Grow Your People

Consider what happens at an initial patient visit: you assess the person with standardized tools and use the results as a baseline for the rest of your evaluation. The results of the initial assessment aren't the only factor in their care plan, but they provide a great starting point.

My friend Stacey thinks I'm an assessment junkie, and she's right. Baseline assessments for my clients include each person's intrinsic motivators. I want to know: What gets someone out of bed in the morning and excited for the day ahead?

A research study conducted by Yoon Jik Cho and James Perry revealed that "employee engagement levels were three times more strongly related to intrinsic than extrinsic motives."[4] Translation: if you engage someone at an intrinsic level of motivation, you don't have to spend as much on financial rewards or other extrinsic motivating factors that impact the bottom line.

For example, if someone is motivated by learning and prefers comprehensive study, give them the chance to be part of a research project that supports the organization. Someone who is motivated by learning only the skills and knowledge necessary for their role would be demotivated by that same comprehensive research project. By understanding individual nuances on this level, managers are better equipped to create meaningful metrics and development plans.

The Career Rock Wall Revisited

Shelly Tyler, co-owner of the Rehabilitation & Performance Institute, implemented a professional development design based on Angela Duckworth's book *Grit: The Power of Passion and Perseverance*. During the new hire phase, she works with individuals to cocreate a professional growth pyramid that identifies the person's ultimate goal, as well as the smaller goals necessary to achieve it. Shelly recognized that if she knows her people's motivations and goals, she can help them grow.

The idea of small goals to reach an ultimate goal is the foundation for building a career rock wall, which I touched on briefly in Chapter 2 in relation to People First THINK. Many healthcare practices have a relatively flat organizational hierarchy for promotion. A career rock wall provides opportunities for growth and development that may not otherwise exist. By keeping your head up to see who is eager to learn and stretch in new directions, you keep people motivated to work toward activities that matter to them.

Every team member's rock wall will look slightly different because it's a reflection of his or her individual goals for growth and development. Based on that personalized information, you can build a career rock wall that places interconnected learning opportunities near each other to ensure that no single move is such a large leap that the person falls. Just like a rock wall in a gym or a rockface in a cliff, a career rock wall isn't static. As the person climbs, he or she might notice different handholds to grab on to or ledges to reach for. There are always options and choices for the next best move.

One of my clients had a great clinician on staff who wanted to become a supervisor. She'd never been in a leadership role before, but she was fantastic with the patients. My client had already identified the soft and technical skills necessary for the supervisor role, so she was able to help her clinician climb toward her goal.

Together, they created a rock wall that included foundational handholds such as mentoring a student, leading a small process improvement project, and becoming a coach for new hires. As the clinician became skilled in these areas, my client added more handholds to strengthen additional managerial skill sets such as tracking and evaluating data, joining the selection interview process, and taking on a larger process improvement project. By the time a supervisor role became available, the clinician was poised for success instead of having to learn everything on the job.

You never know what someone's career path looks like until they have traveled it. The more skills they develop, the easier it can be to move along the path. Jane Palmer's career as a practice administrator at Pennsylvania Retina Specialists is the epitome of a rock wall's effectiveness. While her evolution occurred with different organizations and she didn't know at the onset that she wanted to be a practice administrator, she speaks with pride about her trajectory. She started in medical transcription and moved to clinical technician before shifting into supervisory roles. Building skills and knowledge with each position, she gradually honed her leadership skills advancing to her current role.

Working toward a promotion isn't the only way for people to grow and develop. Consider a biller who wants to do something more within the company. You discover in a quarterly one-on-one that he loves to write, so you add a handhold on his career rock wall to coordinate the monthly patient newsletter. He starts to collect stories from colleagues and patients and publishes them on the company's blog. These activities won't lead to a promotion because there's only one level up from where he is. The real win is that he's engaged with the organization, and he's been given a creative outlet to contribute in ways outside of his immediate job description.

As an owner or a leader, there is an added benefit for the rock wall. Having people take on different tasks and roles that excite them frees up your time. You are successfully delegating in a meaningful way that supports the individual and allows you to stop doing everything yourself.

Annual Acceleration Plans

Annual reviews are my final soapbox for the growth and development cairn of engaging and empowering your people. I know I've convinced you that nomenclature matters, and reviews are one element of growth and development for which I'd love to find a better name. Yes, annual reviews are a discussion of the past year, but if you've been consistent with your quarterlies and feedback throughout the year, the past should take about fifteen minutes. The rest of the hour can then be devoted to goal development for the coming year.

One of my colleagues thinks annual reviews should be renamed "annual acceleration plans," and I'm inclined to agree with her. This is the ideal time to build the career rock wall for the year ahead and even forecast for the next several years. One key benefit of creating professional development goals is to reinforce that your organization offers a culture of growth and learning. It's an opportunity to walk the talk of the People First approach.

Nomenclature matters when it comes to measurements as well. Instead of a numeric scale with significant subjectivity between numbers, use clear language. A simple and clear way to show people how consistently they are demonstrating the desired behaviors that support the organization is with a frequency scale—for example, "John demonstrates X behavior 80% of the time." Utilizing the success factors from the key accountabilities matrix as your baseline, you can objectively document what it means if someone isn't meeting the requirements and what needs to improve.

You might choose to use a system that ranks team members as novice, intermediate, or expert. Novice doesn't mean bad; it simply means the person isn't at the level of an expert. In fact, there are times when novice or intermediate is the appropriate level for the person's tenure and experience. Through continuous training and development, you can move people from novice to expert while ensuring they stay engaged in your organization.

Engagement Surveys: The Elephant in the Room

I call engagement surveys the "elephant in the room" because people love them, hate them, and often use them incorrectly. The data alone doesn't provide the whole picture when it comes to measuring and addressing engagement. While simple in concept—and a measurement like any other—the results of employee engagement surveys are often ignored, misinterpreted, or misused. It's a little bit like taking an X-ray and then ignoring the results. What is the value of the X-ray if what it reveals is not acted upon? What if someone who doesn't know how to interpret the results attempts to create a treatment plan based on a faulty interpretation? What if that X-ray reveals something that biases the reader against the patient? These are some of the same dangers with employee engagement surveys.

I worked with an organization that issued an employee engagement survey with—wait for it—fifty-five questions! Yes, *fifty-five questions.* I asked the leadership team how they were able to create action plans and move the organization forward with so much information. Turns out, they weren't doing much action planning with the data or moving the orga-nization forward.

Together, we worked to streamline the engagement survey down to nine questions that gave us valuable and actionable information. Then I offered training to the frontline man-agers on how to take the results back to the team, facilitate discussions for deeper understanding, and assist in develop-ing action plans. Next, we used one of their leadership off-site retreats to formalize the action plans and assign owners for each item plus due dates and metrics for success.

Once people on the frontline started to see real changes based on their feedback, they started to bring more ideas forward. We did pulse surveys to see which initiatives were working and which weren't. The result was—you'll never believe it—engagement!

Not only do many surveys ask too many questions, but they also ask the wrong ones. I've seen surveys that ask: Do you believe your pay is appropriate for the level of work you do? Even if the results were a resounding "no," if the organization isn't planning to change anyone's pay, why ask? I've also seen surveys that ask employees to describe their "feelings about X, Y, or Z." Focusing on how someone feels in the moment doesn't provide the objective clarity needed to make gains.

Instead, focus on trust and behavior such as the leader's ability to listen, communicate clearly, or respond to feedback. Address whether meeting structures meet their needs for communication and collaboration. Determine whether the organization is actively supporting people's growth and development.

Focus on trust and behavior.

Don't worry about whether you have national benchmark data to which you can compare your internal data: your first survey is your benchmark. Also, don't assume people are dishonest with their answers.

If the organization has clearly and thoroughly articulated the purpose of the survey, the anonymity of the survey, and the way the information will be used to create improvements, honesty should not be a concern.

Many companies are simplifying their surveys to gain real-time, valuable, actionable insight. Scott Judd, the head of people analytics at eBay, says, "We've found that simply asking people how long they intend to stay with the company is twice as accurate for foretelling future turnover than ... predictive analytics."[5]

Another company streamlined their engagement survey to one net promoter score question: How likely are you to recommend to your friends that they work at our practice? Employees give the question a rating and a text box is provided for further comments, which provides rich information about what the organization is doing well and what needs to be improved. That single data point is a crystal clear metric for their scoreboard.

One of the best ways to ensure you continue to grow is to measure where you are compared to where you want to go. Regardless of the results of your engagement surveys, consistency and timing are key, just as they are with meetings.

The Cost of Disengagement

Employee disengagement is usually the result of misalignment, misinterpretation, and/or miscommunication. While many of these issues are addressed through organizational design, even the perfect design won't work if you don't have skilled leaders to initiate and implement People First systems and activities.

A group of physicians was surprised to realize how little time they actually spent with their patients during office visits. While mapping the patient journey, they were able to clearly see how many other people in the office interacted with the patient, and it was a light bulb moment. They suddenly had a newfound appreciation for why the entire staff needed to be engaged in the work, or the patient experience would suffer.

A second light bulb moment occurred when they were shown the financial implications of disengagement. A 2016 Gallup study revealed that actively disengaged employees cost organizations $3,400 for every $10,000 in salary, or 34%.[6] This number is tied to lost productivity, poor communication, or unclear decision making. Sixteen percent of employees at any given organization are actively disengaged.[7] Contrarily, highly engaged teams are 21% more productive and have 41% less absenteeism.[8]

I see these statistics play out with my clients all the time. In fact, it's part of the reason they call me. Some of the common challenges I hear are that work isn't being done correctly, mistakes are rampant, patients are frustrated, the staff calls out with alarming frequency, turnover is high, and they feel like they're putting out fires all day. Even if you aren't experiencing a walkout, are you experiencing a slowdown?

Does it surprise you to know that medical error rates and workers' comp data are direct indicators of engagement? If people are disengaged, the likelihood of accidents increases. Disengaged workers are typically distracted. They tend to choose shortcuts when they don't see the value of the procedures as written. They might put more energy and time into complaining to coworkers than providing focused attention on patients or daily tasks.

Research states, "A synergistic effect exists between-employee engagement and decreased levels of workers' compensation claims for improving patient safety culture."[9] Analysis of Press Ganey data reveals that better employee engagement correlates with better outcomes in safety, technical quality, length of stay, and readmissions.[10]

In both this chapter and the last, I've shared best practices to align, inspire, engage, and empower your team. These activities and attitudes will allow you to create a brand that

attracts top talent so that you are able to select from the best—
which is the topic of our next stage in DO.

Self-Check: Engage and Empower

As multiple studies show, employee engagement (or lack
thereof) is a key deciding factor for your organization's success. If people are rushing for the door or actively disengaged
on the job, you'll never achieve operational sustainability, let
alone a culture of learning and empowerment. Turnover sows
discord, strains the remaining staff, and sucks time, money,
and energy from the whole organization.

Take a close look at your processes to assess them, using
these questions:

1. Have you mapped out a key accountabilities matrix for
   each position that includes desired activities, priority level,
   amount of time to be spent, and the determining success
   factors? More importantly, have you met with everyone
   individually to discuss their matrix?

2. When was the last time you offered training beyond the
   technical skills of the job?

3. If you administer engagement surveys, do you do so in a
   consistent and timely manner? Do you have a clear strategy for actions to sustain or improve your baseline?

4. Does each team member have a professional learning and
   development plan that includes a career rock wall?

5. Are your quarterly meetings building engagement and connection to show how you support your people?

9

Attract and Select: The People First Approach to Recruiting and Hiring

REFRAMING YOUR MINDSET from recruiting to attracting is an imperative if you want to move past "hiring whomever we can find." I think of recruiting as net fishing: you throw out a net and hope something good swims in. Recruiting is passive: attracting is action-filled because it's a direct by-product of aligning, inspiring, engaging, and empowering the people who already work for you.

Sharon Soliday, of The Hello Foundation, offers proof that attracting people is the result of having well-balanced People First THINK, SAY, and DO. In her article "Entrepreneur Truth Telling in Telehealth," she wrote: "The future wealth of this industry is not related to the software with the most bells and whistles. The future of telehealth belongs to the company who masters building a culture reflecting: 1) Easy recruitment[:] 'I want to work with THEM' and 2) Individual professional support."[1]

The Hello Foundation has ninety team members, provides care across six states, and has grown to be worth $6.2 million.

Sharon says the company is thriving because *"in a tech-enabled world, we get the people piece"* [my emphasis]. Because she invests in the later phases of the employee lifecycle, her budget for recruiting is minimal; people come to her asking for jobs. Knowing how to coach and support her team enables her to attract instead of recruit. Also, her turnover rate is in the single digits.

The US Bureau of Labor Statistics reveals that in 2020, the average tenure for healthcare, nonhospital workers was 2.8 years.[2] This data is unrelated to the strength or weakness of the job market. In fact, the People First approach holds true in a boom or bust economy. I devised it during a booming economy with historic lows in unemployment. Practice owners told me they couldn't hold on to people because there were just too many job options. Trust me, people weren't leaving for the $1 an hour increase. They were leaving because they weren't engaged in their work environment.

In contrast, I started writing this book during a recession. Businesses tend to think they have the upper hand during times of high unemployment because employees have fewer options. I'd argue that's when employers need to be extra-careful because when times are tight, people will stay at a company even when they are unhappy. Sure, they are physically present, but they will do the bare minimum of the work required to avoid getting fired.

You can't grow your business with the minimum. It can grow only when people give their best, independently look for ways to advance the practice, and improve patient care.

Job options or no job options, I want people knocking on your door for the opportunity to work with you, bring their best talents, and feel empowered to be successful. Don't you want that, too?

Attraction: The Benefits of Brand Management

When talking about attracting the right talent, Julianne Brandt, COO of Spooner Physical Therapy, uses the term "brand management." She explains that the internal brand and the external brand are reflections of each other. Spooner Physical Therapy is able to attract the ideal talent for the practice. She says, "Attracting the right candidates allows us to drive the business forward because we have the right people."

By creating a strong brand, Spooner attracted a new director of sports medicine, who made the move all the way from Kentucky to Arizona because the company is so highly regarded in the physical therapy world. Julianne says they took the time to build a rock-solid "why," core values blueprint, and treatment philosophy, which fueled their ability to attract the right team members. The core values blueprint reveals the behaviors that support their core values, so they attract people with those behaviors. Potential candidates self-select in or out before they even apply.

The Bureau of Labor Statistics recently revealed that overall healthcare occupations have a projected growth rate of 15% from 2019 to 2029 and healthcare is projected to add more jobs than any other occupational group.[3] Growth brings competition for talent at every level and for each role. Ensure your external brand attracts the types of candidates who embody what your organization THINKS, SAYS, and DOES so you're able to select from the best of the best, instead of whatever the cat drags in.

By demonstrating the behaviors of a People First organization, you will also be able to build a strong reputation in the community as *the* place to work, and thereby attract top-tier talent. You'll be able to move from hiring whoever you can to selecting the best match for the role and the company.

Job Postings: It's a Two-Way Street

Even when your brand attracts highly qualified candidates, you'll still likely post your job openings. Job postings are a key tool to attract the right team members. This is an opportunity to answer the questions all job seekers want to know before applying for a new position: What's in it for me? What's so great about this place? Why would I want to work there?

Instead of listing a generic job description and the minimum job requirements, focus on the organization's values and culture. You want to attract people who are motivated by the type of work environment you have, who live the same values as your company, and whose behaviors will support the culture you've worked so hard to design.

You want to attract candidates who are motivated not only by the work they will be doing but also by the way they will be doing it. One of my clients is starting a new practice with innovative approaches to care that relies heavily on technology, including an app they are developing. The owners are out-of-the-box thinkers, and they want to draw people who are excited by creating new ways of doing things. The job posting highlights opportunities for applicants to be inventive in their role, and uses language that appeals to the types of people they want to attract.

Let's compare and contrast a job posting for the same position, a practice manager, at two very different companies. Although the job description and minimum requirements are similar, that's where the similarities end. Each practice has a unique approach to how work is done, and the job postings reflect those differences.

Practice Manager, Company X	Practice Manager, Company Y
Our company has a rich tradition of excellence in the community. Seeking a manager who will carry on these proven methods.	Our company seeks to provide cutting-edge therapy, and we're looking for a manager who embraces innovation and out-of-the-box thinking.
Our core values include maximizing efficiency and effectiveness for our patients and our practice.	Our core values include selflessly doing what it takes to meet the team's needs.
Looking for managers interested in becoming future owners of the practice.	We provide paid time for researching best practices and support continuous learning.

Both of these companies are successful. They simply function differently and need to attract team members who are excited by working in that type of environment.

Entice candidates by speaking directly to their internal motivators and how they will be met at your company.

People First is a selling point, so be sure to mention how people are rewarded, measured, supported, developed, and encouraged. Let candidates know that your organization puts its own people's needs before patients'. Job postings should communicate not only what people will give but also what they will get in return.

People First is a selling point.

Selecting the Right Candidate

"You seem like a good fit" is a statement that every HR professional hates, and for good reason. "Fit" is an incredibly subjective word. The one, two, or four people involved in the interview process determine whether or not a candidate is "fit" for the role, and that determination is driven largely by their personal opinions.

Beat Back Your Biases

Fit is about "clicking" with someone because of your unconscious biases. To combat any type of unconscious bias, the first step is to become aware that you have them. We all do; and they can impact our ability to make the best possible decision, especially when it comes to hiring and assessing performance potential within any phase of the employee lifecycle.

Rather than falsely believing you can eliminate biases from your psyche, focus on mitigating their impact by recognizing when they come into play. To further complicate matters, there is more than one type of bias. Do any of the following thought patterns sound familiar?

- **AFFINITY BIAS:** The tendency to like someone because they share similar interests or experiences, which makes it easy to think they will do well in the organization. Going to a similar type of college or sharing certain hobbies (boating, rock climbing, running) does not automatically mean the person has the skills or will demonstrate the behaviors that are most beneficial for the role. *TIP:* During the interview process, note areas of common interests or experiences that are not related to success in the role, and then set them aside.

- **CONFIRMATION BIAS:** The tendency to search for, interpret, favor, and recall information that confirms or supports one person's prior beliefs or values.[4] We make decisions about who people are based on their name, where they've worked before, or where they're from. The goal of the interview then becomes to confirm that our assumptions are right. We don't want to learn anything about the person that doesn't reinforce our assumptions, so we look for data that supports our view. We try to find information or "proof" that our belief structure is the correct one. *TIP:* Create a system of standardized interview questions that prevent interviewers from hunting for confirmation of their bias. Focus the structure of the interview on identifying skills and behaviors that are important to the role.

- **ATTRIBUTION BIAS:** The tendency to judge or falsely assume something without knowing all of the situational factors or the whole story. This bias is simply jumping to conclusions with only a few facts. *TIP:* If you aren't clear on the entire situation, ask for clarification and seek to understand the situational factors. Don't assume that because you went to the same college, you got the same grades.

To reduce the risk of making biased decisions, it is imperative to utilize tools that are Equal Employment Opportunity Commission (EEOC) compliant.[5] When I benchmark a role with clients, we use EEOC compliant tools from SHRM to "avoid adverse employment practices that appear neutral but have a discriminatory effect on protected groups."[6]

I've been guilty of making decisions based on my own unconscious biases—we all have. One time, during an interview, I falsely assumed someone's clinical skills were weak because the person had worked in a facility with a terrible reputation. By asking the right questions, I learned the candidate chose to leave that facility specifically because she was frustrated by their lack of focus on quality. This new information brought attention to my bias, and I was able to move past it to make a more informed decision.

Another time, someone arrived at the interview dressed unprofessionally. I had a cursory ten-minute conversation with the person but resolutely determined, "I would never hire someone who wears leggings to a job interview." After she received my rejection letter, the candidate emailed me an impressive note about why she wanted to work for the organization. She followed up a few days later with a phone call to find out what it would take to be hired in the future. Trying to stay within the legal bounds, I explained that we had standards for dress, and I needed to trust people to appear professional at work. She told me she had worn an outfit that was "typical at her previous job," and didn't realize its impact. I brought her back in, for a real interview this time, and discovered she was passionate about the setting and had the right blend of skills. I came very close to missing out on an ideal candidate because of my own bias.

It's not uncommon to think a candidate is the perfect "fit" because they are "just like Jane," the person being replaced. Maybe you'll spend the entire interview looking for confirmation that the person is or isn't like Jane. But do you *really* want someone identical to the person who is leaving? Maybe Jane was good at her job, but was she really, truly excellent in all aspects of it? More importantly, if Jane left because she didn't like her boss, her coworkers, or the culture of the organization, her identical twin replacement could end up leaving for the same reasons.

I argue, emphatically, that the subjective "fit" method is not ideal. Let's discuss a more comprehensive method that is.

Job Matching: An Objective Assessment Tool

Selection should be an objective process. TTI Success Insights says, "Job matching is the science of carefully defining superior performance for each position and then using objective criteria to determine who is selected."[7] To that end, your hiring model needs to look at four critical areas where the candidate and the job need to match (see diagram on page 150):

1. Technical skills and knowledge

2. How they behave

3. Why they do what they do

4. Soft skills

Let's be clear: no candidate will exactly match all four components, but job matching allows you to examine the candidate from the context of the "ideal," identify the gaps, and make a thoughtful decision. This is similar to the common practice of assessing technical skills with a checklist. If someone lacks a technical skill, you evaluate if it's a must-have or something the person can be trained on later.

The DISC assessment allows you to understand people's behavioral style and communication preferences. Assessing behavioral tendencies doesn't mean you're looking for a team of identical robots. It simply means that if someone's natural behaviors are aligned with what's needed for the job, they'll have an easier and more fulfilling experience in it.

Behavioral tendencies evaluated in the DISC profile explain:

* How someone responds to problems and challenges
* How someone influences others to their point of view
* How someone responds to the pace of the environment
* How someone responds to rules and procedures set by others

HIRING & PERFORMANCE MODEL

Skills & Knowledge
Hard skills are the least likely to guarantee performance. They are important but also easily taught if the drive, behavior, and talent is already in place.

Competencies & Talents (What?)
Competencies are those soft skills that come naturally to a person. These can be developed.

Performance Potential

DISC Behaviors (How?)
Behaviors are the way someone takes action, communicates, and does the job. Behavior is adaptable.

Values, Motivators & Drivers (Why?)
Drivers and motivators are the foundation of performance. What a person values and is passionate about will drive their behavior.

Acumen (Can?)
Acumen measures a person's capacity to think clearly. What they think about is above; how they think about what they think about is found here.

Some behavioral styles are better suited for certain roles than others. A decisive and venturesome person will be more successful as a leader than a back-office person focused on process work. Likewise, a solitary, fact-loving person will probably enjoy bookkeeping more than an outgoing, people-oriented person.

It's important that the team represents a diversity of behavioral styles, particularly in leadership. Without diversity, the team will lack certain valuable traits. Consider a scenario in which your team is constantly starting projects that never get finished. What could be the reason for such a trend? It's possible you hired a team of people who are implementers and ready to move forward on an idea. Implementers tend to get distracted by the next new opportunity. Without someone on the team whose strength is to finish projects, great ideas start to pile up.

I once worked with a team of all finishers. They were all great at following projects through to completion. While finishing is a great characteristic, this behavioral style tends to be risk-averse. They struggled to start projects, and within two years, they had completed only one strategic objective.

One practice owner knew she was primarily a visionary and made sure to hire people who could fill in her gaps. She hired a "right-hand woman" who was uniquely skilled in execution; they were able to balance one another's skills to ensure the owner's vision was met. Similarly, at Rehabilitation & Performance Institute, each of the owners brings a different skill set that balances the others and allows for greater success.

What technical and soft skills, behaviors, and inherent motivators are necessary for the role you're hiring for? What do you need more or less of on your team for balance? Map it out.

Interview for THINK

I once received a call from a practice owner who was concerned because her turnover rate during the first year was particularly high. She and her partner determined that the problem was their interview process, so they added three more people to the process. Think about how much money and energy they lost by having *five people* spend hours of their time interviewing candidates because they thought two people weren't enough. No amount of money or energy can save you from a bad design.

A good interview is not about testing someone's endurance skills by inundating them with interviewers. Nor is it about validating their technical skills. It's about determining what and how the person THINKS. Does the candidate's mindset match the organization's? Ask the person how they would contribute to the mission, vision, and values. Include a discussion of the position's key accountabilities and focus your questions on gaps in the benchmark.

As you design your interview process and questions, think through the following considerations:

- What competencies are you are looking for in the role?
- What behaviors are necessary for success in the role?
- How would you describe success for the role?
- What is the organization's mindset (THINK)?
- What are the organization's core values?

The actual interview questions should explore how candidates will respond to certain situations. Ask probing questions that require people to think critically about their experiences and how those experiences impact what they do.

Before you start, ensure that everyone involved in the interview process has been trained on how to ask questions and interpret the answers. Then, build a standardized set of interview questions based on the behaviors, motivators, and competencies from the benchmark.

Utilize an introductory question that sets up the skill, behavior, or experience you want to examine. From there, dig deeper with powerful questions that begin with "how" and "what." The following graphic offers an example of how a series of interview questions might flow.

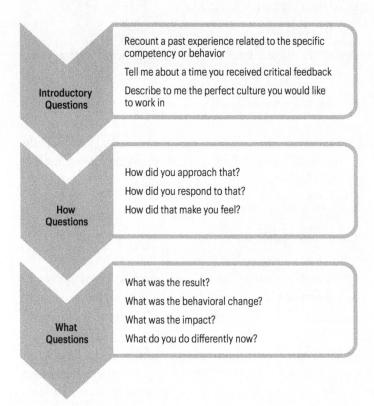

Introductory Questions

Recount a past experience related to the specific competency or behavior

Tell me about a time you received critical feedback

Describe to me the perfect culture you would like to work in

How Questions

How did you approach that?

How did you respond to that?

How did that make you feel?

What Questions

What was the result?

What was the behavioral change?

What was the impact?

What do you do differently now?

Rehabilitation & Performance Institute created a list of interesting interview questions that reveal specific characteristics, and they use a 1 to 4 rating scale to assess the candidate's responses. Some of those questions are listed here.

1. **UNDERSTANDING:** How was your relationship with your last boss? What is one thing you could have done to make that relationship better?

Does not recognize/blames boss   1   2   3   4

Good social awareness/made changes to enhance the relationship
                                        1   2   3   4

2. **GRITTY:** What is your favorite hobby? How long have you been doing that?

Passion and perseverance   1   2   3   4

3. **POSITIVITY:** Tell me a little bit about the past year. What do you anticipate for the next year? (Looking for accomplishments, involvement, and positivity versus negativity.)

Poor vision/experiences   1   2   3   4

Confidence and growth   1   2   3   4

Don't rush the interview process because you desperately need someone on the front desk. Selecting someone who will be engaged in and contribute to the long term goes beyond hiring someone who is willing to be retained. Like all aspects of the People First approach, a well-designed process of attraction and selection should be anchored in what is best for the team and the organization as a whole.

Self-Check: Attract and Select

Attraction and selection, as you've learned, is mostly a by-product of the other DO functions within the employee lifecycle. Without alignment, inspiration, engagement, and empowerment, attracting and selecting ideal candidates could be an obstacle.

Before we turn our attention to the leadership DO factor, conduct a self-check on your attraction and selection processes to ensure you're poised for success.

1. Are you recruiting or attracting top-tier talent to your organization?

2. How are you managing your brand's reputation both internally and externally?

3. If you suffer from high turnover, have you calculated the costs in both time and money?

4. How intentional are you with your job postings? Do you craft them with the same attention you would a piece of marketing literature? Do you highlight the benefits people will experience working for a People First organization?

5. Do you make decisions based on internal unconscious biases? (Hint: the answer is yes. So, what can you do about it?)

6. What tools are you using to make objective versus biased hiring decisions?

7. Do you have a fixed system for interview questions that uncover a candidate's mindset? Is it in alignment with the organization's THINK?

A key takeaway for attracting talent is to protect your rep by putting your people first. It's just good business. The People First path relies on what you THINK, SAY, and DO to create an organizational design that is prepared to GROW into the future.

10

The DO Leadership Factor

L EADERSHIP DO IS about practicing the behaviors that reinforce your THINK and SAY. It's about walking your talk. Though this chapter focuses on many of the behaviors associated with leadership DO, I recognize that behaviors and attitudes cannot be worn like a one-size-fits-all lab coat. You need to tailor them so they fit you.

One of the toughest things about writing this book was the feeling that I was shortchanging the leadership sections. Knowing that one book can't do justice to the entire topic, I chose to highlight foundational skills upon which you can build: being authentic to yourself, emotional intelligence, flexibility, and more. Often overlooked, developing these essential DO skills ensures a sturdier baseline from which to GROW.

Authenticity: Be More You

My first director of rehab position, at age twenty-seven, was exciting for a few reasons. I'd always dreamed of being a *director*—yes, emphasized because the title was important to me. I didn't know what it meant to be a leader, so my intention was to play the part of leader. (This is why mindset matters. In leadership, if your mindset is not squarely rooted in People First, you're playing a part.)

One night, when I was out with friends from work, one of the PTs said, "I wish people could see you like this at work." I laughed and said, "At a bar, having a drink?" She answered seriously, "No. Laughing, having fun, and being a little silly." Her comment was an eye-opener for me. I thought I had to be serious and formal at work. I was stuffed into a suit and stuffed into behaving in ways that weren't natural and, quite honestly, weren't effective. I was an actor, playing the part of a *director*, and not very well, apparently.

Once I discovered a leadership style that was authentic to me, I started to loosen up. I changed how I dressed and became less stuffy. I became more me. I went to music therapy sessions to play the triangle, created Joint Commission Jeopardy for survey prep, and joked with patients and team members. I was "laughing, having fun, and being a little silly." And a funny thing happened: people trusted me more when they knew my words and actions were real—when I stopped acting the part of a leader.

Another way of saying authenticity is "personal leadership alignment." It happens when you land on a way of being as a leader that reflects who you are. While you may admire certain leaders, you can't *be* them. If you try to build your leadership cairn exactly like someone else's, you won't have a true trail marker for your own success.

Fill Your Own Cup

Before we go any further, remember, on the People First path, YOU are People, too! You matter. If you aren't taking care of yourself, you won't be able to take care of others.

People First organizations require leaders with clear heads and hearts, who are rested and healthy. It's easy to fall into a stress trap and feel like there's never enough time to get anything done. You can't increase the number of minutes or hours in a day, but you can manage your energy level. Think about the parts of your life that bring you joy and the parts that frustrate you. What can you do more or less of? Build rituals and routines into your life that are restorative. Pay attention to when your energy stores are low and take a day off. It may sound like an impossible indulgence, but it's actually a necessity.

I know an association president who was afraid the board would be in trouble if she wasn't there. She and her husband hadn't taken a vacation in five years because she felt she couldn't leave work. With changes to the organizational design of the board, she was finally able to go on vacation. She could enjoy herself because she took the steps necessary to redesign the functions within her organization and carve out a little time for herself.

Taking care of your whole self is the one and only thing that *only you can do*. Almost everything else can be delegated to others.

Internal Work for Outward Action

The outward actions of leadership DO begin with internal work. In Chapter 9, we explored the importance of understanding a candidate's inherent motivations, behavioral tendencies, and soft skills. Objective data isn't just for employees; it's an effective tool for yourself, as well. Understanding what inspires you, how you excel, what triggers your emotions, and what natural behavioral tendencies help and hinder your leadership allows you to make choices for your own success.

We all have blind spots when it comes to ourselves. Take a good look in the mirror. What are you doing to motivate your staff and yourself? What do you bring to the table? How do you behave, and does it reflect what you THINK and SAY? Putting yourself under the microscope might feel uncomfortable at first but a little self-examination is proactive preventive care.

Emotional Intelligence

Lexico.com defines emotional intelligence (EQ) as "the capacity to be aware of, control, and express one's emotions, and to handle interpersonal relationships judiciously and empathetically."[1] It's defined elsewhere as the ability to recognize, understand, and effectively manage our emotions to facilitate high levels of collaboration and productivity. In both cases, thoughtful reflection is the foundation.

Unlike behavioral tendencies and inherent motivations, which are for the most part fixed, EQ can be developed. Simply put, emotional intelligence is a skill, a competency of leadership, and, like all skills, it can be improved if you work on it. EQ is recognized as one of the key drivers of performance success; a recent Udemy report showed that 88% of employees value emotional intelligence in leaders.[2]

Daniel Goleman's Theory of Emotional Intelligence has five components: 1) self-awareness, 2) self-regulation, 3) social awareness, 4) social regulation, and 5) motivation.[3] When skilled at regulating emotional responses, you can stay clear-headed in challenging situations. That calm and clarity in thinking allows you to make better decisions despite what is happening around you. You can focus on collaboration instead of addressing disruptive behaviors.

Four of the five components of EQ are explored in the sections ahead.[4]

Self-Awareness and Self-Regulation

Self-awareness is the cornerstone of emotional intelligence. It is our ability to understand what we are experiencing (elation, sadness, anger), what triggers it, and what the impact is. Identifying and tracking triggers helps us 1) notice when we are having a strong response, and 2) understand what triggered the emotion.

I've included a few steps here to master self-awareness.

1. **TRACK SITUATIONS THAT ELICIT STRONG EMOTIONS.** For one to two weeks, pay close attention to your emotions. Name and identify your feelings; write them down. Notice when you have a response that was or wasn't helpful in a particular situation and then work backward. This isn't about whether you were excited when your Amazon package arrived; it's about intense feelings of joy or frustration in response to specific events. Once triggered, these intense feelings can impact your behaviors.

2. **IDENTIFY THE TRIGGER.** Many of my clients attribute an emotion to something on the surface. The trigger often stems from something deeper. You can't respond appropriately if you don't understand what is happening and why, so dig into the emotion to find the root cause. Remember my story about the flood? My trigger was a comment someone made: "We're not essential." That statement caused me to close myself off from any further concern from the team.

Once you understand what triggers you and why, you can focus on the DO of self-regulation. Managing your reactions allows you to stay in control and do the work that needs to get done, instead of being held hostage by what you're experiencing internally.

Develop your skills of self-regulation through following steps:

1. **SEEK FEEDBACK.** Initially, it may be difficult to recognize when you are having a strong reaction. Sometimes, your colleagues notice your reactions even if you don't. For example, you might not feel your face grimace, but they will see it. Seek their feedback on how you respond to triggers.

2. **FIND A BETTER WAY.** Once you understand your responses, resolve to give a better response next time.

3. **PRACTICE.** There are many methods to manage your reactions. Experiment to find the one that works for you.

Social Awareness and Social Regulation

Think about people who can "read the room." Social aware-ness is having your antennae up to observe communication cues that may reveal other people's emotional experiences. Be aware, however, that you can never know for certain what someone else's emotions are. You can only make an educated guess by observing their responses.

The same people who can read the room also seem to wield the power of influence over others. That power stems from combining social awareness and social regulation.

In leadership SAY, you experimented with Level 3 listening skills, which heighten social awareness. Here are a few other things to try:

1. Observe the other person's body language to see if you can interpret their emotional response.

2. Ask for confirmation that you are interpreting the situation and their emotions correctly.

3. Focus on their perspective instead of projecting yours onto them.

4. Empathize with their experiences.

The DO of social regulation is about relationship manage-ment. The more you understand others, the easier it is to engage them. Practice the following:

1. Coach others on their emotional intelligence.

2. Role model teamwork by being helpful and respectful.

3. Find common ground. Encourage people to share their perspectives.

4. Engage in productive conflict resolution practices. Assist team members to find ways of sharing their opinions as part of a collaborative problem-solving process.

Flex and Bend

Self-regulation extends beyond emotions. Understanding your own behavioral tendencies, as well as your team members', allows you to flex and bend to meet others where they are. You don't need to break with who you are; you simply need to adapt to ensure that your interactions with others creates a connection instead of a barrier. Flexing and bending is about adjusting what you DO, not what you THINK. Your mindset and intentions will always be the authentic foundation of your behaviors and words.

So how do you stay authentic while adapting to other people for improved communication and collaboration? Carol and Jacob offer two approaches.

Carol is naturally bold and direct. She is quick to share her thoughts and ideas. A risk taker, she is determined to succeed by staying focused on the task in front of her and being decisive. These natural behavioral tendencies are part of what make her a successful business owner. They are also part of her challenge when connecting with her less assertive, more cautious, and quieter team members.

Because Carol is aware of how her natural tendencies are perceived, she flexes her style. Recognizing that not everyone makes quick decisions or is ready to share thoughts at a meeting, she sends meeting agendas and pertinent information in advance, which gives people time to think about the issues and come prepared with ideas. In everyday exchanges, she starts her conversations by focusing on the other people instead of getting right to business.

Jacob is outgoing and people-oriented. He loves a good party and enjoys being friends with the people he works with. He feels good when everyone else feels good. Preferring to focus on the big picture, Jacob isn't very detail-oriented, but as a business owner, he knows certain details are important. For years, he told his fellow owner, "I trust you, so I don't need to know." While his co-owner is trustworthy, Jacob still needs to be able to make his own well-informed decisions. Jacob knows he gets distracted easily, so when he meets with his partner, he puts away his phone so he can stay focused. He recognizes that asking questions helps him stay on track.

Not only do both Carol and Jacob know who they are, but they also know the people on their teams. They adjust their own styles to foster collaboration and communication. They also demonstrate a high level of emotional intelligence because flexing and bending requires both awareness and regulation.

They pay attention to the triggers that cause them frustration. For example, Carol used to get highly annoyed with the "slow people who couldn't keep up in a conversation." Recognizing that the quieter, more cautious team members triggered a strong emotion, she got curious and learned that her irritation was caused by a simple difference in behavioral tendencies, nothing more. Once she understood that, she was able to regulate her response (flash of anger) to the trigger (thoughtful, reflective people who were not quick with answers). She could flex and bend to make the situation work for everyone.

Pause

Carol's story includes a core aspect of leadership DO: the pause. After identifying the trigger, she paused for a moment before responding. Pausing is an incredibly valuable, and often overlooked, tool. In Carol's case, a short pause between having an emotion and responding to the situation allowed her to realign her collaborative intention with her actions. Pausing lets her keep her emotions in check and gives space for trust to develop. In her case, the pauses are both brief (maybe thirty to sixty seconds) and effective.

Dr. Nancy Buffington, a Boise-based public-speaking trainer and coach, uses the acronym AIR to describe the pause.

A: Acknowledge or Awareness
I: Interrupt
R: Reflect or Reframe

AIR starts with awareness of self and others (keys to high levels of EQ). Acknowledging the need to pause, you can then interrupt the thought so that you can reframe it, replace it, or reject it. I love this acronym because in moments when I need a pause, I also need to take a breath. I may need to physically move to get some air—anything to delay an impulsive response that may have a detrimental effect.

One of my clients uses pauses for another purpose. During brainstorming and problem-solving discussions, she is generally quick to land on a solution. Rather than rushing to share her thoughts, she waits to hear from the team. Pausing in this type of setting allows my client to do several things:

- Ensure that team members develop their own critical thinking skills.

- Convey that she wants them to come up with the answer instead of relying on her to know what to do.

- Allow a flow of ideas she may not have thought of.

- Build self-efficacy, autonomy, and independence.

- Give people the confidence to solve their own challenges.

I know the silence of a pause can be awkward and uncomfortable. As a natural talker, pausing felt anything but natural to me. But knowing its value, I started using props to remind me to sit in the silence. For example, I rarely go into a discussion without a cup of water in my hand. After I ask a question, I take a sip to prevent myself from accidentally talking. During brainstorming sessions, I sip water periodically to allow space for others' ideas.

Do whatever works for you to build a pause into your interactions. Learning to allow space for others is an important part of the leadership journey.

Scheduling: How to Be Everywhere at Once

If you are a practice leader with multiple locations, it can be challenging to visit each clinic with regularity. You probably feel pulled in a lot of different directions. If this sounds like you, get used to the idea that your office will collect dust because you're living out of your backpack from one location to the next. How do you balance getting your work done and being everywhere at once?

Yes, you have budgets, payroll, and reports galore, but taking care of your people is the biggest success factor for the business. When going to each location, don't guess what people want while you are there: seek their input. Do they want to see your face so that they know you see them and their challenges? If yes, bring tea and doughnuts for their huddle. Focus on listening to their needs. Do they need your input for projects? Block your schedule to allow for working meetings.

Be as consistent and transparent as possible with your schedule. By establishing a regular schedule for each location, team members know when you will be there to answer nonurgent questions. It will also prevent you from spending too much time at your favorite clinic or ignoring other clinics. Transparency means people won't be left to wonder where you are or what you're doing with your time. Be sure team members know the best way to get in touch with you when you aren't there.

The primary function of leadership DO is to create an environment in which people feel supported to develop and GROW: grow as individuals, grow the team's initiatives, and grow the organization so it may fulfill its mission. The synergy of a well-balanced People First cairn provides the momentum to GROW in whatever direction you would like to go.

Self-Check: Scheduling Time for People First

As a practice owner or leader, you have a million things on your schedule and that doesn't even include all of the things that pop up each day. So how do you have time to be a People First leader? It comes down to scheduling.

Look at your calendar and conduct a self-check on where you are spending your time.

1. Are you scheduling time to fill your own cup?

2. Have you added quarterlies, rounding, and huddles as a way to connect with the team?

3. Does your schedule include time with each location or area of the practice?

4. Have you scheduled time for your own professional development?

5. Do you have blocks of time to work *on* the business so that when you are *in* the business, you can focus on your team and their needs?

If your current schedule isn't what you'd like it to be, start changing it over time. Instead of trying to move everything this week, simply look at the next few weeks and start blocking time for the different People First activities you want to incorporate. Maybe you are going to add a strategic planning day. Even if it is next month, schedule it now so that you don't fill your calendar with other things.

For many team members, their patient calendars are built weeks in advance. It might take time to add them in because you'll need to block not only your calendar but also their patient calendar.

As your week gets busy, it can be tempting to cancel these People First activities, so mark them in a different color. When you see that color on your calendar, you'll think twice before moving it.

FOUR

GROW

11

Plan, Execute, and Learn

G ROWTH IS A subjective concept based on your personal goals, purpose, and vision. Business growth can come in the form of revenue, volume of patient visits, number of clinics, and more. Regardless of how you define it, growth is about knowing where you're going, having a plan for getting there, adapting to changing circumstances, and learning from wrong turns. It's about moving forward.

The phrase "If you aren't growing, you're dying" has been attributed to a variety of people, and the truth of the statement can't be denied. Dying is the inverse of growing. It doesn't necessarily translate to closing the business; it can be "death by a thousand cuts." Perhaps you're unable to add a new location because you can't find the right people to staff it. Or you can't buy a new piece of equipment because your costs are already outpacing the budget. You can't take vacation because you are short on providers. Patients are frustrated by long wait lists but you can't seem to increase efficiency to add more visit slots. You can't add a new service line because high turnover means your energy is focused on training new hires.

Don't get caught in a death trap. On the People First path, GROWING translates to planning, executing, and recalculating. The organizational cairn will stand without GROW, but it will not stand as tall, and when the path becomes difficult to see, the taller the cairn, the greater likelihood you will find your way out of challenging times.

This chapter demonstrates how to design a growth-oriented culture through strategic planning, execution, and review. It's about making mistakes and learning from errors instead of abandoning sound ideas or becoming stagnant out of fear of mistakes. Supported by the foundational rock of the People First mindset and intentions, you can reduce the severity of your growing pains by taking care of your team.

Set Your GPS: Strategic Planning for Success

GPS is an incredible tool. I don't know how we used to get anywhere without it. It tells you the fastest route by identifying traffic jams and speed traps and, for the most part, gets you where you're going. Working through a sequenced model, GPS first requires an intended destination. Then, examining outside factors that impact the route, it determines the best path forward with step-by-step instructions, including milestone markers along the way.

The choice to use a GPS determines if your journey is haphazard or consciously and purposefully created. People in my area love to go out for a "Sunday drive." They don't use a GPS because they drive for the simple enjoyment of it and to see where they might end up. While they may find somewhere new and interesting, they may also get lost, which they see as part of the fun.

When growing a healthcare practice, getting lost isn't fun—using a GPS is a must. You can't GROW if you don't know where you're going, so setting a clear destination—your goal and vision—is the first step. Begin by reviewing your People First mindset, intentions, and mission.

A board president called for my help because people weren't showing up for meetings and work wasn't moving forward. She worried the board would be in trouble if they didn't act fast. Interestingly, when I spoke with the people on the board individually, they all seemed to understand the importance of the work. The problem was that they didn't feel connected to it.

Step one was to revisit the mission, which wasn't worded in a way that inspired the group to do the work. We went back to mindset and intention to redesign their mission statement. We spent about four hours talking about what everyone loved about the organization. People shared stories of when they felt most impacted by their team members, and at the end of the conversation, they were invigorated toward their purpose. It wasn't simply a chat about the good times; it was a structured way of leading people to the organization's true intention.

Organizational Data Measurements: Metrics Make All the Difference

Just as individual roles need success factors, owners and leaders need tools to measure organizational success. There are several resources to determine which tracking method is best suited to your organization's size and structure. Scorecards from *The 4 Disciplines of Execution* by Chris McChesney, Sean Covey, and Jim Huling (a book I referenced earlier), are one of my favorites, but there are many others that explore key performance indicators (KPIs) and objectives and key results (OKRs). It doesn't matter whether you are an owner, a director, or a clinic manager; you've got to know your numbers. A simple and complete tracking system ensures the data is readily available. Pick a system and stick to it.

One of my clients showed me her haphazard list of fifty different goals for the year. It reminded me of a traditional job description in its laundry list approach; it didn't include success measurements or priority indicators. We got to work to identify her organization's priorities for one, two, and five years. For the first time ever, they had metrics for success, action plans and processes, key milestones, and ownership for each goal. This was a breakthrough moment for them because they developed an actionable plan they could work toward and measure themselves against.

> What you measure is what you get.

Regardless of the planning and measuring tools you use, don't neglect the People First data. Most businesses think employee satisfaction scores are the only data point to measure engagement, but that is not the case. For a more complete picture, include retention rates and turnover by position and by tenure.

If you have a larger organization, consider data that reflects the number of internal promotions over the course of a year. This can help identify if there is enough attention focused on individual growth and development, as well as if leaders have the skills to recognize talent and coach that person to be successful.

What you measure is what you get. So, you need to ensure that your metrics are aligned with the pillars of your organization. If you SAY you care about quality outcomes, that metric needs to be part of the plan. If you SAY your organization is People First, individual success factors need to be included in your measurement system.

Processes to GROW

Many business owners are comfortable creating metrics for success, identifying who is responsible for what, and frequently reviewing their plan. While these activities are absolutely necessary, there is a tendency to overlook a critical factor: the processes that will get you where you want to go. Even an award-winning plan will not get you to your destination if you don't have the processes that fuel the journey.

For example, let's say HR designs a wonderful new coaching tool. If they fail to design a process to roll it out—including training—at best, only a few people will use the tool correctly. At worst, people won't use the tool at all, and those who attempt to use it will do so incorrectly. You need a systematic approach to your processes that supports the promise of a strategic plan.

The board president I mentioned earlier needed help with her organization's processes as well. We designed a system to track successes and discuss challenges. This initiative included redesigning the meeting structure to include a two-and-a-half-hour quarterly review devoted to focusing on the big picture. They used that time to assess the current state of the organization as related to the strategic plan and recalibrate when needed.

Over the next two years, the organization saw dramatic growth. They experienced a higher completion rate of their goals. The team was engaged and more fiscally responsible than ever before. The treasurer told me, "For the first time ever, board members are asking about the financial impact of a strategy they want to try."

Even if you are a small operation and the only leader, it's still important to devote the time to creating a strategic plan. A fellow solopreneur and I meet up once a year, in an interesting location, to work through our individual strategic plans. It helps me tremendously to talk my ideas out with someone and take her challenging questions into consideration. The annual experience has provided me with far more clarity than I could have achieved on my own.

While the process of strategic planning takes time, I can assure you it is well worth it. In many ways, a strategic plan is to an organization what a key accountabilities matrix is to an individual employee. It offers clarity on the priorities and defines the success factors necessary to achieve them. Engaging the entire leadership team in the development of the strategic plan leads to valuable discussions, increased engagement, and, ultimately, buy-in.

Executing the Plan: Team Charters

Once you have a thoroughly developed strategic plan, the next step is to execute it. The entire team should be involved, to move the organization forward and grow in a responsible, intentional manner.

For the execution stage of strategic planning, I swear by the use of team charters. A team charter is a document that spells out a project's specific mission, vision, and goals. It is a structured way to provide clarity on what is expected from the team and ensures they are aligned with intentions, behaviors, and language. The team charter should identify several important elements:

1. Project team's mission and goals
2. Team member roles, responsibilities, and skills

3. Possible barriers to success
4. Ground rules regarding assignments, meetings, and communication
5. Potential sources of conflict
6. Metrics for success

For every LAMP Institute for Leadership program we teach,[1] we request feedback from the participants, and at least one person says the team charter was their "aha" moment. It's a practical and tactical way to gain alignment right from the beginning. And though it can be created quickly, the results are long-lasting. It's like preventive maintenance on your car: thirty minutes to an hour for an oil change can save hours and days down the road.

When I taught organizational behavior at Loyola University Maryland, my students used team charters for their group presentations. They also wrote reflection papers that analyzed their group's success. I found it interesting when four people from the same group acknowledged that they would have been more successful if they had referenced the team charter *during* the project. They had dutifully created a charter stating each team member's strengths and how they would resolve conflict, but when things went awry, they didn't use the charter to get back on track. Having a plan and failing to execute on it is a common pitfall, but I was happy my students recognized their error, which is a great way to learn for next time.

Recalculate in Real Time

Have you ever missed a turn while driving and heard your GPS say over and over again, "Recalculating route"? That's exactly what needs to be built into your strategic planning process—a consistent method to assess if you missed a turn, made a wrong turn, or if there's an accident up ahead. While recalculating is retrospective—you don't know you missed something until it's in the past—the GPS immediately starts to look for alternative routes. Design multiple check-ins to ensure you're on the best route and make adjustments if needed.

While quarterly meetings are an opportunity to pick your head up and look at the big picture, quarterly isn't frequent enough in healthcare. There are faster and simpler ways to gain real-time data for performance assessment such as poker chips, stickers, and other measuring sticks. Here are a few suggestions.

- Ask your patients for their feedback on your new checkout process. Place a bucket by the exit door, ask them to select a green chip if they had a good experience and a red chip if they didn't and toss the chip into a bucket as they leave.

- Ask your staff to select their favorite new uniform style. Give everyone a sticker and have them put it next to their choice.

- Ask the staff if the new workflow process is improving their efficiency. Suggest they use a red, yellow, or green dot on a poster board for a quick pulse check.

A quick assessment doesn't need to be complex or time-consuming. If 90% of the chips regarding the new checkout process are red, you can dig deeper about what's not working. If there's a clear favorite for the new uniforms, you've gotten everyone's input and heard all of their voices. These data points allow you to recalculate in real time, instead of putting decisions or changes on the back burner.

Mistakes Will Be Made

Think about every muscle in the body. In order for that muscle to grow strong, there needs to be repetitive challenge, which creates micro-tears. These tiny injuries to the muscle fibers kick the body into healing mode, allowing the muscle to grow even stronger. And so it is with organizational design.

As you design and redesign your organization, you will make mistakes. They are part of the growth. You won't get SAY and DO right every time, either, and that's OK. Focus on the lessons learned for next time. Failure is not making a mistake; failure is when there is no learning after the mistake.

I'm not saying that mistakes don't have consequences—they do. Even great lessons cost time, money, and energy. But organizations can become efficient at learning from mistakes. That efficiency can translate to anticipating mistakes before they happen by looking far enough down the road and preventing some of the mistakes along the way.

I joked with my Loyola students that our classroom was a lab where they were allowed to "fail fast and fail often." I wanted them to know that failure was an option because it leads to growth. I wanted to help them see that the faster and more often you fail, the more quickly you learn and get better.

By building a mindset that acknowledges mistakes with the intention of turning them into learning opportunities, you communicate that yours is a learning organization. You will remove people's fear of trying new things or of challenging themselves. As Winston Churchill reminded us, "Perfection is the enemy of progress."

My colleague always says, "Well, Amy, you either win or you learn. What was the lesson?" Her question used to frustrate me the same way the GPS "recalculating" voice did. Now, I ask myself that question all the time. I've even gotten to the point at which I'm thankful for mistakes because of the lessons they provide.

As a physical therapist, I spent much of my classroom time in labs, making technical mistakes on classmates before I ever attempted that clinical skill on a patient. Healthcare is hands on, and if you don't get it right the first time, practice, practice, and practice some more, always asking, "What did I learn? How am I going to modify what I did?" Then try again.

> "Perfection is the enemy of progress."
> WINSTON CHURCHILL

Your organizational design should approximate those lab classes. To be clear, I'm not talking about using direct patient care as a lab session, but the other aspects of your design should be explored experimentally. Maybe you tried a new workflow and it didn't work for your team. Instead of saying, "Well, that was a bad workflow" and tossing it out completely, determine what lessons you learned from the experiment, modify, and try a different way.

Create a Flywheel of Learning

In his book *Good to Great*, Jim Collins introduced his concept of the Flywheel Effect. By definition, a flywheel increases a machine's momentum and builds a reserve of available power. Collins teaches us that the Flywheel Effect is a way to increase the energy stores available to your business until a breakthrough occurs.

When you design an organization that sees itself as a grand experiment, you also build a flywheel of learning. It's a circular process during which mistakes create momentum for learning and growth. Think about the energy created when a team member makes a mistake, acknowledges it, says, "Let's try again," and the organization supports them through all of it. Imagine the energy created when a leader acknowledges their mistakes and learns to do better.

I worked in a health system that had just begun to introduce LEAN methodologies for continuous improvement. The first project we tackled for redesign took almost a year. And what a year it was! While the goal was to redesign a process, the larger vision was to teach the team the essential skills of planning, learning from failure, and continuous improvement. Once we learned those skills, we had great momentum around our ability to design, implement, and assess for achievement.

That said, knowing the healthcare education system as I do and seeing what my private-practice clients experience, I recognize that a method of learning from mistakes doesn't come naturally, and we don't learn it in school.

Let's examine two methods for structuring an iterative continuous improvement process. Both require a mindset of curiosity with the intention of learning and growing. Use these methods as an experimental launching point to GROW.

After Action Reviews (AARs)

An AAR is a simple and powerful tool when utilized with the right intention, frequency, and timing. Used in the military, AARs ask four pointed questions that occur as close as possible to the timing of the action or event.

Educate the entire team about AARs and how they work so everyone understands the ground rules as well as their role in the process, up to and including follow-through on the results.

1. GROUND RULES

- Focus on learning, not assigning blame. AARs are about what, why, and how, not who.
- Have a neutral facilitator, preferably someone outside of the situation or someone trained in facilitating AARs.
- Use a standardized template for AARs.
- Hold the AAR as close as possible to the actual event.

2. KEY QUESTIONS

- What was supposed to happen? (The plan, the intended results, and/or the goal)
- What really happened? (The results or outcome)
- What caused this result? (What did we learn? Compare the planned outcome versus the actual outcome)
- What can we do better next time? (What should we stop, start, or continue? Change, sustain, or modify for the future?)

3. FOLLOW-UP AND FOLLOW-THROUGH

- Remember, the organization is a learning laboratory.
- What are some opportunities to test what we've learned?
- Who is responsible for the next trial and what do they need to know in order to be successful?

Important to note: AARs aren't only for mistakes; they are also an effective way to debrief a success. As a bonus, using them to debrief successes removes the stigma that AARs are a punishment when something goes wrong.

Plan-Do-Study-Act (PDSA)

PDSA is a process improvement method attributed to management consultant W. Edwards Deming. While Deming worked in the manufacturing industry, the model is applicable anywhere and is often used in healthcare research.[2] Because it is the preferred method of healthcare research, it is also applicable to healthcare practices.

Originally, the process was based on an acronym for Plan-Do-CHECK-Act, but Deming later changed the wording. He felt that "check" implied inspection over analysis.[3] Personally, I love the modification because the process is about analyzing what is working or not and making adjustments. It's not about inspecting the work for the sake of inspecting.

PDSA is as straightforward as it sounds. Here's how it works.

1. PLAN

- What problem am I trying to solve? What question am I trying to answer?
- Build the plan: who, what, when, where, and how
- How am I going to collect data to study later?

2. DO

- Try out the plan
- Collect your data
- Document the results including successes, problems, and surprises

3. STUDY

- Compare the results to the plan
- Summarize learning
- Modify the plan for next time
- This is a great place to initiate the AAR

4. ACT

- Stop, start, or continue based on the modifications created in Study
- Move into the next cycle of PDSA (it is an iterative process that keeps going through trials)

It's not surprising that consistency and frequency are the keys to both of these models. A well-facilitated AAR can take thirty minutes. Certainly, PDSAs take longer but the planning and study phases can be sped up through practice. By establishing the use of these tools to assess both positive outcomes and mistakes, you create a pattern where the team becomes accustomed to the true goals and nature of process learning. The flywheel of learning gets faster and faster. Share what the team learned by developing a structure for reporting. Don't overlook a discussion about risks and concerns, as well as your plans to address them.

As we all know, healthcare is changing all the time. In order to adapt to the changes, we need to learn what works and what doesn't. Creating a culture of learning begins with developing methods of analysis (such as the PDSA cycle or AARs). Once leaders can successfully facilitate the learning process, they can focus on developing the team's willingness to take risks and adapt to change. This willingness is a key to GROW and a function that we will discuss in depth in the next chapter.

Self-Check: The Stop/Start/Continue Method

There are times when we do such an excellent job of planning and executing that we just keep those processes going forever. Eventually, there isn't enough time in the day for all of these great activities, and we need to decide what to eliminate to make room for what our practice needs today. A simple and effective way to make this decision is with the "stop/start/ continue" method.

STOP
- What isn't working anymore?
- What things are impractical or impede other work?
- What isn't delivering the right impact?
- What is a duplicate of another process?

START
- What needs to be done that isn't currently being done?
- What is worth trying or experimenting with for better results?
- Will it reduce waste?
- Will it add value?

CONTINUE
- What's working well?
- What needs more time to start working?
- Do we like it or need it?

12

Change Is the Only Constant

THE CLEAREST PATH to successful growth, as you learned in the previous chapter, must be well planned. Knowing where you're going and how you'll get there is critical to avoiding pitfalls and wrong turns along the way. Though pitfalls and wrong turns are virtually inevitable, they can be minimized. You can reduce the severity of your growing pains by having a keen awareness of what's happening around you. Managing change may seem as elusive as a compliant patient but this chapter provides strategies you can use to be more successful with change.

Change Management: Get Ahead of It

The best leader I ever worked for quoted W. Edwards Deming when she said, "It is not necessary to change. Survival is not mandatory." She was right. We don't *have* to change. But if we want to survive, we have *to be willing* to change.

Who really likes change? Me, me, pick me! I *love* change. Truly, my behavioral style is off the charts when it comes to pioneering new ways of approaching work and optimistically trusting it will all work out in the end. I love working with organizations in need of a turnaround as much as I love working with companies on the bleeding edge of something new.

Many of my clients share my pioneering spirit, although theirs is typically tempered with realism and motivated by ROI as opposed to the pure fun of the change process. Some prefer steadiness, but they recognize that in order to survive, the company needs to do something different. My role is to help them structure the processes that will allow them to change and thrive.

> Sixty-five percent of managers have change fatigue.

Like most industries, the pace of change in healthcare has increased dramatically. Yet, the majority of healthcare providers have a behavioral tendency toward a slower pace of change. The desire for steadiness and consistency is becoming unrealistic in healthcare due to rapid changes in technology, policy, regulation, and reimbursement. Plus, we have staff shortages and increased demand for consumer-style healthcare that exhaust the team. To pile change on top of the other challenges feels overwhelming. Recognize that 65% of managers have change fatigue, and their level of fatigue isn't decreasing with time.[1] Let's explore tools to cope with and get ahead of change and change fatigue.

The Five Components of Change

D. Ambrose's graphic interpretation of change (shown opposite) depicts change in a visual and manageable way.[2] He shows that clear actions create reactions, or outcomes. The graphic's simplicity and comprehensiveness provide a method of assessing what is required for successful change. This approach fosters the People First mindset by recognizing that people are not the hindrance to change: they are the catalyst.

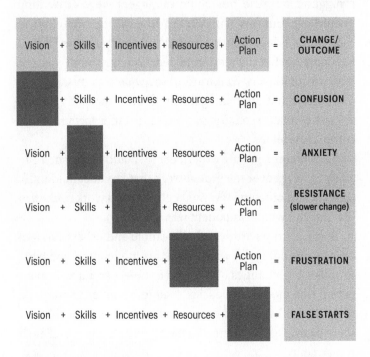

Vision	+	Skills	+	Incentives	+	Resources	+	Action Plan	=	CHANGE/ OUTCOME
	+	Skills	+	Incentives	+	Resources	+	Action Plan	=	CONFUSION
Vision	+		+	Incentives	+	Resources	+	Action Plan	=	ANXIETY
Vision	+	Skills	+		+	Resources	+	Action Plan	=	RESISTANCE (slower change)
Vision	+	Skills	+	Incentives	+		+	Action Plan	=	FRUSTRATION
Vision	+	Skills	+	Incentives	+	Resources	+		=	FALSE STARTS

The five components of change are presented across the top: vision, skills, incentives, resources, and action plan, which lead to the outcome of successful change. The far right column includes several rows of alternative outcomes: confusion, anxiety, resistance, frustration, and false starts.

Each of the five components is a critical checklist for success. If you get one of the alternate outcomes, you can determine which component was overlooked or missed altogether, and how to address it.

While the ideal situation is to initiate change with all five components in place, I'll share an example of how to use the grid while in the midst of change. A client was struggling because her clinic managers weren't holding people accountable with regard to expectations—that is, they weren't documenting within the required time frames. Recognizing that the managers' reaction (outcome) was anxiety, we could work backward to see what was missing. We discovered that the managers didn't have the skills for productive conflict resolution or the tools to build accountability within their teams.

The outcome you are experiencing should be part of a gap analysis to uncover the groundwork that lies ahead. Identify your current outcome (far right column) and work backward to figure out what component was missed.

Some changes are seemingly simple and others can feel overwhelming. Don't wait to use this model until you have to make big changes. The better skilled you are at navigating this model, the easier change becomes to manage, regardless of its size or scope. In the five sections below, I share examples to underscore the applicable aspects of each component.

Vision

In change management, vision is not only about *what* we are trying to change; it's also about *why* we are trying to change it. As you well know by now, the People First approach is built on THINK. Recall the organization's mindset and intention when making changes. What is the intention of the change? Does it reflect your mindset? How do you honor People First during this change process?

Example: Vision for a new location

A new location adds revenue and expands your owner-ship vision of growing market share. This type of change requires a vision that encompasses not only what you will gain, but also what the team and the people they serve will gain. Your vision is about serving more patients and becoming a center of excellence in the community, both of which encompass the "why" behind the change.

Example: Vision for using new billing software

This may sound like a simple process change, but simple doesn't always mean easy. Changing software can feel like a nuisance to the team. Help them understand *why* you are moving to a new system. Does it make the billing process less confusing for patients? Will it make processing payments less time-consuming? Be clear on how the process change assists the organization in achieving the overarching goals for the patient and the practice.

What about a larger organizational change such as a shift in practice patterns or adding a new service? Show alignment between the shift and the long-term goals of the practice. If people seemed confused about the change, going back to the vision makes it easier for people to stay focused on *why* you are doing it.

One of my favorite books about change is *Switch* by Chip Heath and Dan Heath. They advise readers to "shrink the change" into smaller, bite-sized visions. Instead of tying a change in practice patterns to the long-term vision of "eliminating healthcare inequality," build a vision for each step of the change process.[3]

The desired outcome must be clearly articulated: when we do X, the outcome will be Y.

Skills

Without the proper skills, people will have anxiety and fear about adapting to a change. Imagine a manager's anxiety if you tell them they need to coach a staff member, but they don't have coaching skills. It's the same as asking a provider to suture if they've only watched someone else do it. Don't ignore the need for soft skills that decrease the anxiety, fear, and pressure of change management: resilience, flexibility, and use of PDSA or other tools for reflective learning.

Example: Skills for a new location
> If you are an owner adding your first manager at a new location, you'll need skills in delegation, priority management, and how to lead other leaders. If your current staff is training the team for the new location, be sure they have coaching skills in addition to teaching skills.

Example: Skills for new billing software
> When people think about new software, they think about the technical skills needed to operate it. Think beyond technical skills and instead ask yourself if the leadership team has the skills needed to create a clear rollout plan and learning modules to make training easier. Do they know how to ask powerful questions and listen to ascertain how well the rollout is working? Do they know how to implement AARs or the PDSA cycle to evaluate how the new software process implementation is going for the people who have to use it, and how to make adjustments accordingly?

With any change, there will always be one or two people who like the old way better. Regardless, ensure that every team member has the skills to efficiently and accurately use the tools required to do the job.

Many organizations believe that teaching skills once is enough. Training at the onset of a change is usually intense and consistent, but then it tapers off. With the excitement and fear of trying something new, people are able to take in only so much learning at once. Or two years down the line, you might notice anxiety creeping back in and you don't know why. Anxiety increases when people realize there is a limit to their skills. It might be time for a refresher. During rounding meetings, confirm what further skill development is needed and then provide additional training.

Incentives

Many organizations tend to focus on money and other extrinsic motivators. Money can work as an incentive for short-term results when change is easy. But when tasks become more complicated, it becomes necessary to tap into people's intrinsic motivators, as discussed in Chapter 8.

Let's say you need to incentivize someone to change a workflow process that's been in place for twenty years. If the person is motivated by efficiency and getting a return on their energy and time, then focus on the parts of the workflow that will streamline the process. That strategy places value on what they value, which motivates them toward the necessary change.

Example: Incentives for a new location

Sometimes, adding a new location has little to no impact on the people who work at the original location, so incentivizing them for success at the new location is unnecessary. Other times, you may need to ask the staff to shift between multiple locations or even permanently move over to the new location. In either of those cases, people need to know what's in it for them. Can they expect a promotion? Will they be closer to where they live and have a shorter commute? Will the whole team of bonded coworkers be moved together? Are you relying on that team's skill and experience to make a positive impact on the community? These are all strong incentives for people to get excited about the new location.

Example: Incentives for new billing software

Be clear about how the new software, once mastered, will make people's lives easier. Help them understand the benefits: less time to complete tasks, fewer patients calling with questions, payments received faster, and so on. Track benefits over the first year because it might take more than a few months to see and feel the positives.

With change management, a perfect execution is unlikely. Adjustments will need to be made. If you incentivize only for a perfect outcome, people may hide glitches or develop their own workarounds instead of coming forward with solutions to make it better. Incentivize for a flywheel of learning over perfection. Reward people who find problems!

> Incentivize for a flywheel of learning over perfection.

A friend of mine worked for an organization that incentivized 100% participation in the employee engagement survey. Sounds great, until she reported that no leaders took the time to consider the results or make changes based on the responses. For the staff, it was simply a task to get through quickly because their answers didn't matter. Of course, a 100% response rate is amazing but only if the data is valid and adds value. Incentivize valuable data by what showing what it can lead to.

In change management, incentives typically last only as long as it takes to execute the initial change. For change to be sustainable and long-lasting, the reward needs to be repeated. It's not enough to offer rewards at the initial launch. Be sure to include long-term incentives in your planning process so people remain committed well after the initial rollout.

Resources

Picture this: You're making dinner. You're elbow-deep in your preparations when you discover you're missing a key ingredient. Now you can't make the dish you planned. You've got to resort to what you have on hand, and it's not going to be what you had in mind.

Resources for change management are the same as ingredients for a dish. To implement your vision, you need the required energy, time, materials, and leadership. Depending on the size of the change, recognize that you might not have all of the required resources on hand. Do you need additional help or coaching in the short term? Do you need to hire additional people with different skill sets? What resources, specifically, are needed to make the change?

Take a thorough inventory in advance of your initiative to ensure you're not caught short. Throughout the change process, check your inventory of resources to see if any are low. Often, projects require greater resources than you initially planned.

Example: Resources for a new location
Consider resources beyond capital, space, equipment, and so on. Owners often hire a skeleton crew for the new location with the intention of ramping up slowly. Yet, so often, I hear, "We got so big so fast." Your staff on the first day should be equivalent to what you'll need to meet the demands encountered in the third month. Otherwise, the new team will burn out and the community will become frustrated by long wait lists.

Example: Resources for new billing software
With any new system, time is the most important resource. Be sure to provide enough up-front training time. Build practice time into your planning before it goes live. You may need to increase your staffing level for the first week or two because people will be at the beginning of the learning curve.

I automatically double the time a recipe specifies for prep because I'm not a fast chopper or measurer of ingredients. Professional chefs write recipes, and they have the skills to move much faster through the kitchen than I do. The same goes for process change. Be realistic in your timeline and allow people some wiggle room to get comfortable.

Action Plan

An action plan is where the rubber meets the road. You may have a vision for the change, the skills necessary to facilitate it, strong incentives in place, and all the resources, but if your action plan isn't well conceived and constructed, you'll experience false starts.

Successful action plans are created before the change is initiated. They may be drawn as a roadmap or other visual, or simply written out. Action plans include the vision statement, time frame, who is responsible for what, what steps must be completed before another can occur, what steps should occur simultaneously, milestones, and metrics. While you may hit the mark with the first action plan, the majority of change initiatives require at least some level of course correction. Remind people at the onset that yours is a learning culture, and while you've made the best action plan possible, you accept that change is a continuous cycle of improvement. The action plan offers a chance to study the results, redesign the action plan, and try again. (Rather than share pages and pages of action plan examples here, I'll highlight components of the plan that cannot be overlooked.)

Example: Action plan for either a new location or new billing software

1. **CELEBRATE:** Plan a celebration for the team after the first week of the change initiative to thank people for getting on board.

2. **WEEKLY PUNCH LIST MEETINGS:** It's imperative to discuss what is working and what isn't.

3. **MONTHLY DEBRIEFS:** Use the PDSA method to evaluate progress on a monthly basis.

4. **CELEBRATE AGAIN:** Big and small wins deserve recognition and celebration. Show people you're interested in the long-term success of the change and you appreciate their work to see it through.

As with every step along the People First path, alignment is key for change management. Planning for and executing the five components of change might seem like a lot of work, but the more you practice, the better you become. Use this model initially on smaller change initiatives until you feel comfortable using it, and then apply it to the bigger changes.

Mastering the five components of change will be essential as your organization GROWS from one stage to the next. And the good news is, growth doesn't need to be something that derails an organization. Its effects, challenges, and necessities can be predicted by understanding the variables that occur within each of James Fischer's 7 Stages of Growth, which we'll look into next.

Self-Check: Change Readiness

The Greek philosopher Heraclitus was eons ahead of his time when he famously said, "The only constant is change." His observation speaks to the infallible and undeniable force of change. It's always there, and it's always coming.

Take a few moments to consider how you and your team are prepared to cope with the inevitability of change.

VISION: How well articulated is the vision for the desired or impending change? Is it in alignment with the organization's high-level vision?

SKILLS: What skills are needed for the work ahead?

INCENTIVES: How are you incentivizing your people to step up during a change initiative, and for how long?

RESOURCES: What resources are needed to execute the change?

ACTION PLAN: What are you doing to avoid false starts and ensure team buy-in? How are you reinforcing a learning culture through your change management practices?

More than likely, you are in the midst of some change, big or small. If you haven't successfully made the change, which of the five other possible outcomes are you seeing from the team? Is the team showing confusion, anxiety, resistance, frustration, or false starts? Work backward across the grid (see page 191) to see what component you need to address. What can you DO or SAY to provide clarity and ensure buy-in?

13

The 7 Stages of Growth

D URING THE PROCESS of writing this book, I interviewed many talented people who have designed phenomenally successful organizations. When asked what they wanted the book to address, they said they wanted to know how to stay on the People First path as their organizations grew.

Fortunately, researcher, management consultant, and cofounder of the Origin Institute James Fischer examined more than 650 small businesses to create a method to predict how growth impacts organizations. In his book *Navigating the Growth Curve*, he identifies seven stages of growth and explains that the number of its people defines the complexity of an organization.[1]

Sure, there are other factors that impact growth. The budget gets bigger and takes more effort to put together. Adding new locations makes logistics more challenging. But people are the number one factor that determines the complexity of the organization. In line with Fischer's brilliant research, the number of employees is the measuring stick by which we are going to determine your stage of growth.

People are the number one factor that determines the complexity of the organization.

Focus On the Right Things at the Right Time

As your organization GROWS, its needs and challenges will change. Even your leadership style will need to adapt. In fact, throughout an organization's life, you'll constantly be reevaluating and redesigning. While this prospect can seem daunting, you can ensure your efforts reap the greatest rewards by focusing on the right things at the right time.

Like many of the topics discussed on the People First path, the 7 Stages of Growth is a huge topic. In fact, Laurie Taylor, a prolific author, the founder of FlashPoint! LLC, and my friend, has written a book about *each* stage of growth. She also created the Stages of Growth X-Ray™. As a certified Stages of Growth specialist, I've seen how effective the X-Ray is for companies large and small.

The Stages of Growth X-Ray™ is a critical tool that allows owners and leaders to:

1. Predict how growth will impact them

2. Adapt their leadership skills, knowledge, and insights to their specific stage of growth

3. Focus on the right things at the right time

4. Keep people at the forefront of their organizational design and leadership

A business in my area acquired another company, and in less than one year, they grew from fifty-three employees to more than one hundred. Moving so quickly through three stages, they missed key challenges along the way. Their leadership team didn't adapt their style or adjust to the new nonnegotiable rules of each stage. It wasn't a surprise when they started to experience difficulties in their business.

I'm not suggesting you pass up the chance to grow. Taking your leadership team through the X-Ray process provides you with a way to understand the needs and challenges of your expanding business, which in turn allows you to meet those challenges head-on. It reveals leadership alignment and misalignment around the aspects in this chapter as well as other nonnegotiable rules for where you are today and the road ahead.

Remember, people are the source of complexity in an organization, even if you don't realize it. In the chart shown here, the number of employees defines each stage of growth.

Stage 1	Stage 2	Stage 3	Stage 4	Stage 5	Stage 6	Stage 7
Start Up	Ramp Up	Delegation	Professional	Integration	Strategic	Visionary
1–10 People	11–19 People	20–34 People	35–57 People	58–95 People	96–160 People	161–500 People

© 2021 FlashPoint! LLC

Builder-Protector Ratio: The Mindset in Each Stage

The ability to grow relies on the right balance of confidence and caution. This balance can be translated as the ratio between the builder (confidence) and protector (caution).

Some people are naturally risk-averse; others thrive on it. Regardless of which comes naturally for you, there needs to be a balance of both. Balance doesn't mean equal parts of confidence and caution. For the builder side of the ratio, the numbers range from 1 to 4 while the protector range is only 1 to 2.

Builder Mindset (1–4)	Protector Mindset (1–2)
Risk-tolerant	Risk-averse
Open to new ideas	Suspicious of new ideas
Challenges the way things are done	Prefers the status quo
Takes on new initiatives	Concerned about the company's financial strength for new ideas
Wants to step on the gas	Wants to step on the brakes

As Laurie Taylor says, "a confident company is a successful company." You've got to be willing to take some risks. While the builder need can range from 1 to 4, there is only one time the builder is less than 2. Of course, you never throw all caution to the wind, but notice the amount of protector ranges only from 1 to 2, with only Stage 4 having the protector at 2.

That balance doesn't necessarily need to come from the owner exclusively. If you have a diverse leadership team, you likely have people who are naturally excited by decisive action toward winning as well as people who are naturally more cautious.

As an owner and leader, you need to know which ratio is appropriate for your stage. If that ratio is not already being met, make the necessary adjustments for success. Too much builder profile (confidence) and the company may overreach and fail. Too much protector (caution) profile and the practice may stall. If the balance is off, excessive optimism or lack of forward movement can cause people to become frustrated.

The Twenty-Seven Challenges: Get Ahead of Them

Throughout your organization's life, you will experience all twenty-seven challenges listed here. Each Stage of Growth has its own unique set of "top five challenges" that need to be addressed. One of the four rules governing the Stages of Growth model is that whatever challenges are not resolved in one stage follow you into the next. Don't let this scare you. By understanding these challenges in advance and when they'll impact you, you can get ahead of them.

1. Profits are inadequate to grow the company

2. Need for an improved profit design

3. Customers are migrating away from your products/services

4. Continual cash flow challenges

5. Limited capital available to grow

6. Employee turnover

7. Hiring quality staff

8. Staff morale and voltage challenges

9. Need for a flexible planning model

10. Need to have better staff buy-in

11. Project management and resource coordination challenges

12. Communication gap between leadership and staff

13. New staff orientation

14. Staff training

15. Unclear values throughout the organization

16. Dealing with the cost of lost expertise or knowledge when employees leave

17. Chaotic periods destabilizing the company

18. Organization needs to understand how the company will grow in the future, not just the leadership

19. Organization needs to better understand the impact staff satisfaction has on the company's profitability

20. Company culture is generally resistant to change

21. The marketplace and your customers change too quickly

22. Difficulty forecasting problem areas before they surface

23. Difficulty diagnosing the real problems or obstacles to growth

24. Too slow getting new products/services to market

25. Not able to quickly get systems and procedures in place as the company is growing

26. Weak product/service development and differentiation in market

27. Challenge expanding sales

While this list is in no particular order, I want you to think about what you consider to be your top five challenges. The exercise at the end of this chapter will let you self-check your ideas versus the research (but don't skip ahead!).

Notice how many of these challenges relate to people and communication. In fact, communication is a root cause of at least one top five challenge in all seven stages.

As you GROW from Stage 1 to whichever stage you aspire to, your system of SAY needs to grow and change with you. Gaps in communication will seem to creep up overnight. Undoubtedly, sharing information consistently in an easy-to-access way becomes more challenging with each new person added to the team. James Fischer's research identifies when these gaps will appear so you can prepare for them in advance. Don't ignore the importance of the regular meetings (discussed in Chapter 5).

Growing with Chaos or Calm

Moving from stage to stage requires a transition period. Fischer's research into the 650 businesses he studied revealed two types of transitions, both of which can create chaos unless you understand why they are happening and what you can do to create calm. Transition zones are caused by increased activity, happen for different reasons, and require different responses.

Stage 1	Stage 2	Stage 3	Stage 4	Stage 5	Stage 6	Stage 7
Start Up	Ramp Up	Delegation	Professional	Integration	Strategic	Visionary
1–10 People	11–19 People	20–34 People	35–57 People	58–95 People	96–160 People	161–500 People

Flood Zone   Wind Tunnel   Flood Zone   Wind Tunnel   Flood Zone   Wind Tunnel

Flood Zones

As you grow, there will be times when things come at you so fast, you may feel like you can't keep up. Fischer refers to these times as flood zones.

When my clients hit a flood zone, they tend to want to add more people to alleviate the overwhelm of an increased workload. That approach makes sense in certain situations, but adding people shouldn't be the first reaction; it needs to be a strategic decision. Every time a person is added, workplace complexity increases, which runs counter to the logic of adding people to make things easier.

In healthcare, there are standard formulas to determine frontline staffing patterns for different practice settings. We have X amount of space, which can accommodate Y number of patients, so we need Z clinical staff to treat those patients. Staff can see X number of patients per hour, so we need Y number of staff to accommodate appointments.

While the strategic approach for frontline positions seems clear, the size of the leadership team gets muddy in the flood zone. Math formulas alone can't determine when to add to the leadership team and what positions to add. So, when is the right time to add another manager or director? I often hear stories of waiting too long, of people almost burning out before saying it is time to get some help.

Consider who is working beyond their capacity and no longer able to perform all of the activities at their highest level. What can you do to alleviate their workload so they can best support the team? I've completed several strategic leadership reviews in which the outcome was not a new leadership position but simply a redistribution of the work and/or a less expensive administrative assistant position. Confirm that workflows are optimized for efficiency so the systems themselves aren't creating a slowdown. It's cheaper to fix a system than hire additional team members.

Wind Tunnels

The flipside of a flood zone is the (appropriately named) wind tunnel. The experience of trying to manage during such times can feel like the wind is pushing so strongly against you that your umbrella flips inside out. What are your options? Continue trying to shield yourself from the elements even though your protective tool no longer works as it was designed? Or stop fighting the wind and let go of the umbrella so you can move forward?

It's natural to try to hang on to the past and keep things as they were, but if you want to grow, it's time to let go of what no longer works in your organization. It could be a leader who isn't willing to walk the People First path or a billing process that can't keep up with the increasing number of patients. It can also be old methodology that was once useful but has lost its benefits.

Think about each of the processes in your practice and why you put them into place. Do the reasons still exist? Is there a cheaper, faster, or better way to do things today and in the future? What processes are missing to grow? Just as with adding people during the flood zone, be strategic about adding or letting go of processes. Utilize the PDSA cycle or stop/start/continue to make small adjustments for the greatest success.

To move through both flood zones and wind tunnels, you can:

- Plan ahead for what you know is coming
- Prepare everyone for what's coming
- Assess what's working and what isn't
- Devise new strategies

Know that calmer days are ahead when you can anticipate the chaos zones, plan for them, and stay focused on the vision.

The 7 Stages of Growth Leadership Factor

Daniel Goleman, Richard Boyatzis, and Annie McKee's book *Primal Leadership: Unleashing the Power of Emotional Intelligence* presents six dominant leadership styles in business. Each style has benefits and drawbacks. A leader's job is to be skilled in each and to know what style to use when. In fact, each stage of growth includes a prioritized blend of three of the six styles. The six dominant leadership styles are as follows:

AFFILIATIVE

- Creates harmony by connecting people
- Builds relationships within the team and represents opportunities for collaboration
- During stressful times or to heal a rift, this empathetic style allows leaders to boost morale by demonstrating that they care for their people

DEMOCRATIC

- Focused on generating new ideas as well as gaining feedback and input from others
- Creates consensus and buy-in from the team
- During times of uncertainty about the direction to take, this style builds commitment through participation

COMMANDING

- Provides clear direction
- Demands compliance with directives (this style can be coercive, so use sparingly)
- During a crisis or if the organization needs a turnaround, this command-and-control style leaves no room for alternatives

PACESETTING

- Focused on achieving excellence and meeting high standards
- Motivates a team by demonstrating excellence themselves
- Used sparingly and best if combined with relationship-based leadership styles

VISIONARY

- Energizes people toward a shared vision or dream
- Creates energy and enthusiasm by tying the vision to the practice's mission and values
- Appropriate during times of change or when direction needs to be adjusted

COACHING

- Focused on team member's personal and professional improvement
- Connects individual's goals to the company's goals
- Least used, most often needed[2]

LEADERSHIP STYLES BY STAGE OF GROWTH						
Stage 1	Stage 2	Stage 3	Stage 4	Stage 5	Stage 6	Stage 7
Visionary	Coaching	Coaching	Coaching	Democratic	Affiliative	Visionary
Coaching	Pacesetting	Democratic	Affiliative	Visionary	Pacesetting	Coaching
Commanding	Commanding	Pacesetting	Pacesetting	Affiliative	Visionary	Democratic

Notice how frequently coaching is the primary or secondary style. Regardless of size, your leadership centers on supporting people.

Whether your organization is at Stage 1 or Stage 7, managing growth in accordance with the People First approach is a strategy that will withstand the floods, winds, and any other chaotic elements thrown your way. Understanding exactly what stage of growth your business is currently in allows you to meet today's challenges and plan for the future.

Self-Check: Identify Your Current Challenges

James Fischer's 7 Stages of Growth model is one of the most useful and effective tools to use to get ahead of your growth curve. By knowing what's coming, leaders are better able to plan and manage the turbulence associated with change.

Revisit the list of the twenty-seven challenges all businesses face as they move through the 7 Stage Stages of Growth (page 207). Select five that you think are applicable to what your organization is facing right now. Now compare your list to the grid below. Here, we see what research shows are the true top five challenges at each stage.

LEADERSHIP STYLES BY STAGE OF GROWTH						
Stage 1	Stage 2	Stage 3	Stage 4	Stage 5	Stage 6	Stage 7
Cash Flow	Hiring Quality People	Staff Buy-In	Weak Project Management	Improve Sales	Staff Buy-In	Products Not Differentiated
Destabilized by Chaos	Improve Sales	Leadership/ Staff Gap	Difficulty Diagnosing Problems	Difficulty Forecasting Problems	Staff Satisfaction/ Profit Relationship Not Seen	Inadequate Profits
Slow Product Development & Getting to Market	Cash Flow	Weak Business Design	Employee Turnover	Cost of Lost Expertise	New Staff Orientation	Slow Getting Offering to Market
Limited Capital to Grow	Leadership/ Staff Gap	Core Values Unclear	Not Getting Systems in Place	Weak Business Design	Weak Business Design	Weak Business Design
Improve Sales	Limited Capital to Grow	Culture Resistant to Change	Organization Uninformed about Company Growth	Staff Training	Hiring Quality Staff	Marketplace Changes Too Quickly

14

The GROW
Leadership Factor

A S YOUR ORGANIZATION GROWS and changes, so too will its leadership needs. While you will always need to lead yourself, you will become a leader of others and possibly a leader of other leaders. Things will look a lot different from when you opened your practice with one front desk person and possibly a handful of other staff.

The transformation along the path to GROW doesn't happen all at once. You may take a giant step forward and then plateau before moving forward again. As we explore how leaders need to grow, remember: there is no one-size-fits-all. Authenticity is of paramount importance in your life and in your leadership.

Please understand: Leadership growth doesn't require that you change who you are, your behavioral style, intrinsic motivators, or your authentic core. Every aspect of your leadership THINK, SAY, and DO remains applicable and necessary. We focus here on how to use those support rocks to GROW through the ranks of leadership and practice changes.

Conflict Is Inevitable: Resolution Is a Skill

Before we explore leadership growth, I want to address something very few people like to talk about: conflict. You may be
wondering why I've saved this topic for the growth section.
After all, growth is the feel-good stuff that inspires us to move
along the path, and conflict is resolved through THINK, SAY,
and DO, right?

The topic of conflict is here for three reasons:

1. Conflicts are inevitable as we change and grow.

2. With growth, mistakes will be made, and those mistakes
   can lead to conflict.

3. For the majority of leaders I've worked with, skillfully navigating conflict is one of the biggest opportunities for growth.

Having to say hard things in difficult conversations goes hand
in hand with leadership. Productive conflict using the People
First approach starts with a mindset you're well familiar with:
coaching people from where they are because all people are
whole. Beginning difficult conversations with this fundamental
People First mindset can immediately defuse a tense situation.

For many types of conflict, the PDSA and AAR tools can
ensure that the focus remains on the process instead of on the
person. Seeking change doesn't mean that the person is bad,
weak, or broken. Blaming someone for a process problem is
the easy way out.

Know your goals for the discussion at the onset. Share
those goals up front and ask the other person to share their
goals for the discussions as well. Once mutual goals have

been established, you have the foundation for a productive discussion. Since you intentionally designed a learning practice, remind the person that the core intention for the discussion is to learn from mistakes and move forward.

Be aware of your triggers and be prepared to self-regulate. Go in with the curious mind, willing to find solutions. With powerful questions and Level 2 and 3 listening, you have the tools to create a rich dialogue that brings all the issues out on the table. Providing the foundation of productive conflict, these elements are also a reminder of all that you have learned throughout this book. Growth includes appreciating what you've learned, practicing the skills, and building for your future success. And now, we move on to other aspects that will contribute to your leadership growth.[1]

The Art of Delegation

Many of the practice owners I work with are nearing a breaking point by the time they call me. They feel stretched too thin. I typically start our work together by having them list everything on their plate and the time it takes to complete each thing. When we look at the list together, we both feel overwhelmed and recognize there is no way one person can do it all.

On one such occasion, my client Elizabeth and I really dug into her list. I wanted to know what she loved and what she hated, what she tended to procrastinate on, and why she felt certain things needed to stay with her as opposed to being off-loaded. She had tried to delegate some of her action items, but it wasn't going well.

To exemplify her frustration, she told me that each clinician was expected to complete at least one blog per quarter, but she "couldn't even get them to do that!" She wasn't inclined to give them even more important tasks from her list if they weren't able to fulfill a simple (and infrequent) request.

After talking with the clinicians, we discovered that they hated blogging, not because of the time it took but because they assumed they were expected to "sell." They weren't trained as salespeople, they argued. They were trained to help patients get healthy and become independent.

With this key information, we were able to reframe the way Elizabeth's clinicians looked at the task of blogging. Yes, blogs could generate interest and bring in new clients, but they weren't intended to be part of a sales campaign. They were intended to educate the community on the many services they offered that could help them feel better.

That small but vital shift in how the clinicians perceived blogs changed their willingness to complete the task. It also freed up a small portion of Elizabeth's to-do list. She began to look for more ways to tap into her clinicians' inherent motivators so she could delegate appropriately.

Delegation comes from the mindset that people are whole and that their work is meaningful to them. The art of delegation goes hand in hand with the career rock wall, covered previously. When you grow your people, you also give yourself the space and time to grow your business.

I worked with a CEO recently who led a robust business. Though he had over seven hundred employees, fifty of whom were in leadership positions, he was still doing the final interviews for new hires, all the way down to the supervisor level. He said, "I will let go of the interviews when I am confident we have a process that will work without me." The CEO wasn't arrogant; he was afraid to let go.

I saw his fear of letting go firsthand when I was working on a project with his Human Resources team. The CEO joined the initial meeting, when we discussed the goals and direction, and told us to move forward. At subsequent project-related meetings, when a decision point arose, HR always said, "I need to check with the CEO on this," or, "Let's get the CEO's opinion." We had to wait for the CEO to respond before we could move forward.

When presented with finished work, the CEO had a list of questions related to matters that had already been resolved three meetings before. We had to take the time to walk him through everything again. In the end, he changed a few words in the messaging but everything else remained the same. The impact: same great product at twice the time plus unnecessary frustration with the process.

The CEO knew he needed to step back. In fact, he *wanted* to step back so he could concentrate on growing the business. But he didn't have confidence in his team to get it right, and they feared getting it wrong. The team was too scared to move anything forward without his input, and he believed he had to stay intimately involved in every decision, process change, and hire. They had created a brutal cycle of learned helplessness and the cycle was constantly reinforced.

> A culture of learned helplessness is no way to move forward.

I appreciate that it was his practice, his vision, his reputation, and—as is often the case—his name on the line. But a culture of learned helplessness is no way to move forward. The CEO had no choice but to learn better delegation skills, which is primarily about what needs to be done and less about how it gets done.

Successful delegation does not occur in a vacuum. You don't simply off-load a bunch of tasks and projects to someone else and never look back. As I've said, alignment is key. The entire team must be clear on the vision, goals, milestones, and measures of success. They must understand the nonnegotiable elements of how to do the project (budget, time, etc.). Then, schedule regular check-ins to review progress, address questions, and confirm that the project is moving in the right direction. Like everything else, delegation requires practice, and mistakes will be made. Use your flywheel of learning, and don't give up.

Lead Your Leaders

Just as your mindset needs to shift from patient first to People First, your perspective also needs to shift from frontline first to leaders first. As you grow, the organizational chart will change. You will become a leader of leaders, and they will lead the people on the frontline. Sharon Soliday, of The Hello Foundation, says, "If you don't let go of leading the frontline, you can't scale your business." She's right, but slipping into a new leadership role and letting go of the old is not without its challenges.

Two practice owners I work with told me they feel like they are constantly getting pulled into everyday operations because "people want to hear from the owners." They have seventy employees, supervisors at each of their seven locations, and practice managers who lead the supervisors.

They intend to continue building their business, but growing from a small practice that "feels like family" to a multilocation operation with multiple levels of leadership can be a tough leap.

Of course, you want to stay connected to the frontline, but it's also necessary to give your managers the space to succeed. One way to do that is to give a new manager a warm handoff. Let the team know they are in good hands and you are confident in the new person's People First approach.

It's hard to remain connected and cut the cord at the same time. Though cutting the cord may be done with the best of intentions—letting the new manager step up and do their thing—it could leave the frontline team feeling as though they've lost someone. They might think you don't care about them anymore. But if you jump in to help the frontline, out of habit or loyalty, and accidentally sideline a skilled frontline leader in the process, you'll find yourself on a slippery slope. Planning times to visit the frontline with the sole intention of connection can alleviate this balancing act. Be sure, when you visit, that you don't step in to solve their woes. Instead, refer them back to the manager to model your confidence in their leadership.

Stepping back to allow your leaders to lead does not mean checking out entirely. Though you are handing over the management of daily operations, you will always need to keep your eye on the big picture. For example, two physician owners I know hired an office manager and a practice administrator so they could continue providing direct patient care. Hiring practice leaders let them focus on their specialty, but it didn't eliminate their need to know the people on their team or what was happening in operations.

Dr. Ron Eaker's practice, Women's Health of Augusta, has six physician owners. At first, they all viewed themselves primarily as physicians, without recognizing their role as owners. In fact, outside of their quarterly board meetings, they knew very little about the operations. When they realized how out of touch they were with the day-to-day goings on in their practice, they made some changes.

Now, they are each responsible for a specific subunit of the business such as finance, operations, clinical care, marketing, human resources. While they aren't managing the daily functions of these departments, they are expected to take ownership for that part of the business. Respecting that they aren't directly involved in the daily operations, they don't insert themselves into other leaders' area of responsibility.

The owners organized themselves like those of a professional sports team, who are aware of what's happening in the game but get involved only when asked by the coaches on the field. Each physician owner stays up to date on the big picture of the practice, but they aren't on the field directing the work. They are leading their leaders by giving them space but remaining connected.

The Long and Winding Road of Leadership Development

My mantra, and the core tenet of the People First approach—grow your people to grow your business—applies to every single person in the organization, especially *you*. As a clinical leader or owner, you've spent your career learning the skills and knowledge associated with your medical specialty.

Chances are, you've had a lot less, if any, education on business and leadership. Your own professional growth must be treated with the same focus and care as everyone else's. The only difference is, for the most part, your growth will be self-directed.

Many practice leaders and owners are great clinicians who either got promoted or decided to strike out on their own. They struggle in their new role because they never received leadership training and coaching. Great clinicians do not necessarily make great leaders. They need to proactively seek the tools to succeed.

Growing as a leader requires that you chart your own path for leadership skill development. Just as you do with your employees, start with an inventory of your existing skills, identify areas that need to be enhanced, and gather input from trusted colleagues and your team. Create your own career rock wall: what skills and handholds do you want or need to create for yourself to grow with your organization?

My clients tell me stories all the time about how much more successful they are with their teams when they are willing to examine areas for their own improvement. It demonstrates that they're able to look at their skills or weaknesses in an objective manner and build a plan for improvement.

When Scott joined one of my leadership programs, he had already been in management for over a decade but he still experienced profound changes through the program. While he always had a People First mindset, developing his soft skills and EQ increased his and his team's performance. There is always more to be learned, and what

What better way to set the tone for a learning culture than for the leader to initiate his or her professional education!

better way to set the tone for a learning culture than for the leader to initiate his or her professional education!

One woman I worked with shared how embarking on the People First path changed her life. She was struggling to navigate relationships with some people on her team who had strong personalities. She had never taken a leadership course and thought that by simply managing the task load, she was a leader.

By participating in a leadership program, she learned the difference between operating a business and being a leader. It was a breakthrough for her. She took ownership of her own development. Like so many who have taken the path to People First leadership, she moved from asking questions such as, "Why can't I get buy-in?" or "Why are people leaving?" to "What opportunities are there for growth?" and "How can I help my people feel valued?" That shift made all the difference. She is now successful in her role as a leader, supporting her team and growing her business areas.

Soft-Skill Competencies

Most organizations do a great job of providing technical skills training but drop the ball when it comes to providing ongoing training on the soft skills, which is a combination of people skills, social skills, communication skills, attitude, and mindset. The void in soft skill training exists at all levels, but it is particularly noticeable at the leadership level.

I share a small sample here of the twenty-five most recognized soft skills, many of which we've already explored. Coupled with EQ, they are among the most important, applicable, and valuable leadership skills that can be developed for productive and meaningful People First focused interactions. It's unlikely you will need to develop *all* of them, but give some thought as to which of these skills would best serve your personal growth and the needs of your organization. The self-check at the end of the chapter takes you through an exercise with all twenty-five skills.

- Decision making
- Influencing others
- Conflict management
- Conceptual thinking
- Continuous learning
- Employee development/coaching
- Time/priority management
- Resiliency
- Creativity/innovation
- Interpersonal skills

Most of these skills are foundational for any leader, regardless of the size or scope of your practice. During certain periods of your career or in certain situations, particular soft skills will be more important than others. For example, if you are considering large-scale changes, well-developed conceptual thinking will be beneficial. The complexity of decision making changes with the complexity of your practice.

Constantly evaluate which soft skills are needed for your role today, and which will be needed in the future. Ensure they are a core focus of your learning and development plan, as they should be for all of your people.

The Many Benefits of Peer Learning

I think of leadership growth on the People First path the same way I view my experience of getting back on the slopes after I hadn't skied in ten years. Sure, I could have just put the skis on and hoped it would all came back to me. Or I could "lose a day" by taking a lesson.

Because I chose to invest the time to learn new skills, practice technique, and get expert advice, the rest of the ski season was extraordinary. I moved quickly to more challenging runs and had a much higher confidence level than expected. The feeling of "getting good" at these skills far outweighed the cost of the lesson, in both time and money. Now, I kick off each season with a lesson or two, which advances my abilities much faster than if I struggled on my own.

One of the biggest stumbling blocks on the People First path is the false belief that it will be faster to just "get it done" rather than waste time learning from others, falling down, and getting back up. Taking the time to learn isn't losing time; it's an important investment in the bigger vision for your company.

One unexpected benefit from my skiing lessons was humility. By saying I wasn't an expert, and by seeking training and coaching, I showed vulnerability and a willingness to learn. An article called "8 Keys to Succeeding as a Physician in Private Practice" by the American Medical Association makes the point beautifully. It says, "A medical degree gives a physician the right to envision owning a private practice, but the skills to open and operate one takes the help of professionals."[2]

Becoming a better skier wasn't something I did alone. I had a coach for the lesson and then I had friends providing encouragement as I practiced what I learned. Surround yourself with other owners and leaders who are on the People First path. Find a squad of experts to provide direction and cheer you on when the going gets tough. You can start by joining the

People First community at thepeoplefirstbook.com. You will go faster and further because you did.

When considering a peer group, don't limit yourself to your immediate experience. Think big and broad. They don't all have to be physicians in the same specialty or therapists with the same size clinic. Find the right mastermind group for your needs. Perhaps join one for first-time owners or owners with multiple locations. One of the most valuable mastermind groups I've been a part of is a collection of people who use the same assessment tools I do, but we all use them for different purposes. It's more important to find a safe space to share fears, weaknesses, and triumphs than it is to be with a group of people in your precise industry.

Different needs call for different expertise. You may need to develop a specific skill set for a specific stage of growth. Find leaders who are managing practices of the size you aspire to be and seek their counsel. If you need to lead through a merger or acquisition, seek coaches and support from people who've been through it. Perhaps you want to sell your business. Find a consultant who specializes in building your company's valuation prior to the sale. If you want to write a book, I'll connect you with the best coaches, editors, and publishers.

There is always someone outside of your immediate day-to-day who can guide you on your path. Don't shy away from professional coaches and consultants. Ask other leaders whom they've worked with and build a list of people you can turn to. I don't know of many professionals in a leadership position who have gotten where they are by themselves. We all need community, support, and a squad of people to push us to new heights.

Leadership growth, just like organizational design, is about having a plan, developing new skills, repeating best practices, and learning from mistakes. And just like growing your business, growing as a leader takes time, exploration, and repetition. Leadership growth is incremental, but when it's built upon the sturdy foundation of People First THINK, SAY, and DO, the sky's the limit.

Self-Check: Building Your Own Career Rock Wall

In order to grow, you need to know where you already have skills and what skills you need to develop. Building your own career rock wall first means an honest look at your current strengths and limitations. In this moment, you have soft skills that are well developed and some that need to improve. Think about where the practice is going: What skills will you need for the future?

You don't need all of these skills for any role. Consider this list of the top twenty-five, as identified by TTI Success Insights, and determine the top seven soft skills needed for leadership success in your practice. Next, consider how well developed your skills currently are: are they developed or moderately developed, or do they need development? Put an asterisk beside the ones you want to focus on improving. Then seek out training, coaching, and peer support. Remember, nobody is perfect, so be honest.

1. **APPRECIATING OTHERS:** Identifying with and caring about others

2. **CONCEPTUAL THINKING:** Analyzing hypothetical situations, patterns, and/or abstract concepts to formulate connections and new insights

3. **CONFLICT MANAGEMENT:** Understanding, addressing, and resolving conflict constructively

4. **CONTINUOUS LEARNING:** Taking initiative to regularly learn new concepts, technologies, and/or methods

5. **CREATIVITY AND INNOVATION:** Creating new approaches, designs, processes, technologies, and/or systems to achieve the desired results

6. **CUSTOMER FOCUS:** Anticipating, meeting, and/or exceeding customer needs, wants, and expectations

7. **DECISION MAKING:** Analyzing all aspects of a situation to make consistently sound and timely decisions

8. **DIPLOMACY:** Effectively and tactfully handling difficult or sensitive issues

9. **EMPLOYEE DEVELOPMENT/COACHING:** Facilitating, supporting, and contributing to the professional growth of others

10. **FLEXIBILITY:** Readily modifying, responding, and adapting to change with minimal resistance

11. **FUTURISTIC THINKING:** Imagining, envisioning, projecting, and/or creating what has not yet been actualized

12. **GOAL ORIENTATION:** Setting, pursuing, and attaining goals, regardless of obstacles or circumstances

13. **INFLUENCING OTHERS:** Personally affecting others' actions, decisions, opinions, or thinking

14. **INTERPERSONAL SKILLS:** Effectively communicating, building rapport, and relating well to all kinds of people

15. **LEADERSHIP:** Organizing and influencing people to believe in a vision while creating a sense of purpose and direction

16. **PERSONAL ACCOUNTABILITY:** Being responsible for personal actions

17. **PLANNING AND ORGANIZING:** Establishing courses of action to ensure that work is completed effectively

18. **PROBLEM SOLVING:** Defining, analyzing, and diagnosing key components of a problem to formulate a solution

19. **PROJECT MANAGEMENT:** Identifying and overseeing all resources, tasks, systems, and people to obtain results

20. **NEGOTIATION:** Listening to many points of view and facilitating agreements between two or more parties

21. **RESILIENCY:** Quickly recovering from adversity

22. **SELF-STARTING:** Demonstrating initiative and willingness to begin working

23. **TIME AND PRIORITY MANAGEMENT:** Prioritizing and completing tasks in order to deliver desired outcomes within allotted time frames

24. **TEAMWORK:** Cooperating with others to meet objectives

25. **UNDERSTANDING OTHERS:** Understanding the uniqueness and contributions of others[3]

FIVE

THE PATH CONTINUES

15

Are We There Yet?

O NLY YOU CAN answer the question "Are we there yet?" because only you know where "there" actually is. It might be:

- Having the confidence to add another location

- A low-drama workplace without fires or chaos

- A practice running so smoothly, you get the highest possible valuation when you are ready to sell

- A practice where people show up every day excited to work hard and change lives

- A practice that is future-proofed against changes and challenges because you have engaged people and systems that support those people's work

- A well-deserved vacation, when you can turn off your phone because the practice can handle itself

- A practice with a harmonious work environment, low turnover, and people asking to work there

- A practice with a team of people who hold themselves accountable for the success of the operation

- A leadership team you trust because they have developed the skills necessary to lead

- A team aligned with a clear mission, vision, and values

So, are you there yet? If the answer is no, that's OK. All of these places are points of interest and possible destinations on the People First path. Wherever you're trying to go, you'll get there.

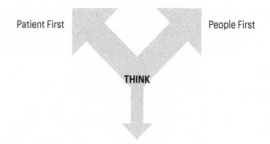

The first step is to ensure you're heading in the right direction. Maybe you're at the intersection of THINK, and you've got a choice to make as to which path you'll take. The patient first path is cluttered with vines and overgrowth that will strangle your business. The People First path is where you'll find the mindset, intentions, language, behaviors, and activities to grow your people so you can grow your business.

Every single practice leader in this book is growing because they recognize that their success is predicated on putting their people before patients. Patients are attracted to the practice because they know they are getting excellent care, and they feel good being there. They feel good because the employees feel good. You simply can't have one without the other.

Once you're firmly on the People First path, the second step is to assess how far along you are. Are your employees fully engaged and empowered, or are you just starting to lay the foundation? When you know where you are, step three is to set your sights on the first mile marker you'd like to reach or change you'd like to implement. Pick something small and explore how it feels. With the momentum of a few mile markers behind you and the open trail ahead, you are well on your way to getting "there." Apply the principles of the flywheel to each step along the path through what you SAY and DO.

By following the People First cairn of organizational design, you can move faster, pivot as needed, and proceed further with confidence. Plus, you're building your personal leadership cairn, which includes helping others build theirs. The more cairns, the clearer the direction. There's nothing and no one blocking the way.

Pick Your Rocks, Test the Stack

Since I started Cairn Consulting Solutions, people have been sending me pictures of cairns. While they all have the same basic design and are solid enough to stand, they are all completely unique. The rocks are different sizes, shapes, and colors: some are smooth, some are rough, some are flat, and some are sharp. Just like cairns in nature, your People First cairn will resemble others' but it won't be identical. It will reflect your unique value proposition, mission, vision, and goals; it will be authentically your own.

One person sent me a picture of her young daughter building a cairn. Kids building cairns offers the perfect example of how leaders and owners should go about organizational design. Kids squat right to the ground, gather the rocks they want to stack, and start experimenting. They pick up a rock, look to see which side will balance, and play around with placement. If a rock falls, they pick it up and try again. They might try a few different stacks, but they stick with it until the cairn stands.

Like children building cairns, I want you to take your time and experiment. I've seen practice leaders who hear about a new program and try to quickly throw it together with a grand announcement. They treat it like a New Year's resolution, and they're surprised when it doesn't stick. Instead of trying to figure out what could have been done better, they simply toss it aside and move on to the next thing. Or worse, they go back to doing things the way they've always been done. Stick with it!

Slow down and be thoughtful about what to tackle next. Redesign your organization by putting the right rocks in the right order. Create the space for deep work so you can truly understand the root cause of problems.

Whenever I go into a practice for the first time, I interview different members of the team. So often, the feedback I hear is about unclear expectations and poor communication. I've never gone into an organization and heard, "We communicate too much," or, "My manager is too clear."

THINK hard about your processes, systems, structures, and leadership style. DO they effectively support the People First approach? How can you better SAY what you'd like the path ahead to look like for the organization and every single person in it as you GROW? How are the rocks in your cairn stacked and balanced, and do they serve as a guide for your people?

Pushback: Confronting the Fear Factor

In my experience, the biggest obstacle to designing a People First organization is not time or money or even desire: it is fear. That fear can manifest in myriad ways. I'll share a few.

A couple of my clients have told me they're attracted to People First design and the general idea of it, but they don't want to create systems and structures that will "feel too corporate." After all, in most cases, they started their own company because they didn't like working for a big organization. I hear this loud and clear. However, systems and structures are not what make an organization feel corporate. It is the overall lack of attention to individuals and their unique needs that gives off the coldness associated with corporations.

Some of my clients have expressed a fear that "structure"— in any formal sense of the word—will feel forced or, worse, inauthentic. It doesn't have to be that way. Structure provides the framework so that team members are clear about what is expected of them and what it takes to succeed. It is a People First leader's responsibility to use that structure to build connection, accountability, engagement, and a culture of learning that supports people to grow professionally both as individuals and as a team.

This book includes stories of organizations as small as three people and larger than three thousand, and they all have systems and structures in place. Systems and structures allow you to scale. Don't resist the idea of systems; resist the idea of systems that don't support the People First mindset.

I've also heard clients get stuck in a "what if?" mentality: What if someone quits? What if I make all of these changes and they don't work? What if I fire Suzy Q and the rest of the team gets anxious? What if I appear weak or indecisive? I've had every single one of these fears myself, and so has every person represented in this book.

The antidote to fear is faith. If you have faith in people, and their potential, and their desire to succeed, to contribute at work, and to grow, then organizational success will follow. Stay focused on your vision of what you want for your people, yourself, and your practice. If there are roadblocks to achieving what you want, remove them.

Incremental Changes

The People First approach doesn't require a grand announcement or a lot of fanfare. You don't need to send an email exclaiming, "There's a new model for meetings and it shows that we put people first!" Simply alert everyone to the new format and agenda, and reiterate the intention behind the new structure in the first few meetings.

There is a lot less pressure when making incremental changes versus launching a whole new model or adopting an entirely new ideology. Look at it as an experiment you're trying out. Create a structure that allows you to fulfill the habits of a People First organization and leader. Identify where you want to start and strategically work through the various aspects of your design and leadership behaviors. Be grateful for mistakes, and ask, "What's the lesson?" so you can do better next time. Be persistent; nobody gets it all right on the first try. As you make incremental changes, you'll begin to pick up speed, moving more quickly and efficiently once you overcome that initial inertia.

The Road Ahead

People often reach out to me and ask, "How do I handle this one situation?" I want to help everyone, so I ask questions and help them decide on an action plan. Then they usually come back with more questions.

The People First path isn't about one situation, one decision, or one person. Moving effectively and efficiently requires a coordinated effort, not a one-time solution to a one-time situation. It's about the way you THINK, SAY, DO, and GROW everything in both your organization and your personal leadership.

I'm on a mission to change the way people experience work. As you well know, that mission is predicated on the knowledge that you need to grow your people to grow your business. My mission is dependent on you, the owner and leader, to design an organization that supports People First. Together, we can make the People First approach a reality for your practice, ensuring success, growth, and perhaps a vacation during which your phone is on silent because there are no fires to put out.

Before you create a People First plan, take a good look at your practice. Get curious and observe it as if you were an outsider looking in.

- How do other people treat each other?

- What words to you commonly hear?

- Do people look harried or are they moving quickly but calmly with confidence?

- How many people are smiling?

If you're reading this book, you're open to the People First mindset. And if you've got the mindset, you've got the foundational rock of the cairn. THINK of the rest of your career as a laboratory, because People First leadership takes a lifetime. And since you know the benefits of being a People First leader by now, you know it's worth the time and attention. Having experienced the joy and rewards of becoming a People First leader, I can assure you: getting there is half the fun.

Acknowledgments

M y JOURNEY TO People First leadership came with hard work, hard times, and an incredibly supportive group of friends, family, and colleagues. I wouldn't be where I am today without my LAMP Institute for Leadership teachers, friends, and fellow committee members Stacey Zeigler, Emily Becker, Beth Sarfaty, Debbie Miller, David Wessells, Sean Bagbey, Dan Dziadura, John Corcoran, Deb Kucera, and more throughout the years. LAMP was a turning point in my journey, and I am forever grateful for all the ways it has transformed my life.

Thanks also to the coaches, friends, and mentors who have helped me navigate business ownership and life in general: Nancy Roberts, Julie Tabish, the Mastermind crew, Candice Frazer, Chris Kenney, Ken Seawell, Laurie Taylor, and, of course, my Golden Girls—Carol, Laurie, Kim, and Jen. And a special thanks to Jen Boucher, who is the best team member I could imagine.

I owe a special thanks to leaders who contributed to my growth and learning: Ron Rothstein and Carol Swartz, the first leaders who showed me what true leadership can be, and Deb Bradley, simply the best leader and mentor I could have asked for.

This book's journey began with my amazing book coach, Stacy Ennis, whose encouragement and guidance created the foundation for the book, but also who, quite simply, changed my life. Brooke White, my content editor, brought my very rough draft to life, helping me effectively share the messages I believe in. She cheered me on, made me laugh, and made me work harder than I knew I could. Page Two then provided the guidance to turn these words into the book I'm proud to share with you today. While serving as my cheerleaders, Amber Vilhauer and her team, including Hannah Tripp and Bridget McElvain, brought their marketing talents to help me get this book out into the world.

I also want to thank the many people I interviewed for this book, whose stories are woven into its fabric: Carla Tocko, Tara Marshall, Dr. Sarah Gerrish, Derek Fenwick, Laura Cantrell, Dr. Nancy Buffington, Laurri Wallace, Terri Nuss, Mike Johnson, Julianne Brandt, Sharon Soliday, Dr. Ron Eaker, Laurie Taylor, Jennifer Peterson, Scott Kucharski, Shelly Tyler, Craig Phifer, Sean Bagbey, Sheila Sparks, Samantha Diehl, Renee Mitzel, Jane Palmer, Chryssa Rich, Mya Beaulieu, and Lou Ellen Horwitz.

And thank you to my clients, who allow me to join their journey. You bring me joy as I see you progress to the next level with your hard work and dedication to People First.

Notes

Introduction

1   See Wikipedia, s.v. "Cairn," en.wikipedia.org/wiki/Cairn.

2   "The IHI Triple Aim," Initiatives, Institute for Healthcare Improvement, ihi.org/Engage/Initiatives/TripleAim/Pages/default.aspx.

Chapter 1: The People First Path

1   Susan Collier, Joyce Fitzpatrick, Sandra Siedlecki, and Mary Dolansky, "Employee Engagement and a Culture of Safety in the Intensive Care Unit," *JONA: The Journal of Nursing Administration* 46, no. 1 (January 2016): 49–54, doi.org/10.1097/NNA.0000000000000292.

2   Nell Buhlman and Thomas Lee, "When Patient Experience and Employee Engagement Both Improve, Hospitals' Ratings and Profits Climb," *Harvard Business Review*, May 8, 2019, hbr.org/2019/05/when-patient-experience-and-employee-engagement-both-improve-hospitals-ratings-and-profits-climb.

3   Jim Harter and AnnaMarie Mann, "The Right Culture: Not Just about Employee Satisfaction," Gallup, Workplace, April 12, 2017, gallup.com/workplace/236366/right-culture-not-employee-satisfaction.aspx.

4   Harter and Mann, "The Right Culture."

5   "History," About Us, Institute for Healthcare Improvement, ihi.org/about/Pages/History.aspx.

6　Thomas Bodenheimer and Christine Sinsky, "From Triple to Quadruple Aim: Care of the Patient Requires Care of the Provider," *Annals of Family Medicine* 12, no. 6 (November 2014): 573–76, doi.org/10.1370/afm.1713.

7　Mike Michalowicz, *Profit First: Transform Your Business from a Cash-Eating Monster to a Money-Making Machine* (New York: Portfolio, 2017).

Chapter 3: The THINK Leadership Factor

1　"What Causes Employee Disengagement?" Employee Engagement Survey, Articles, CustomInsight, custominsight.com/employee-engagement-survey/research-employee-disengagement.asp.

2　"Employee Retention Report," TINYpulse, 2018, tinypulse.com/hubfs/2018%20Employee%20Retention%20Report.pdf.

3　As cited in "New DDI Research: 57 Percent of Employees Quit Because of Their Boss," DDI Frontline Leader Project, Cision, December 9, 2019, prnewswire.com/news-releases/new-ddi-research-57-percent-of-employees-quit-because-of-their-boss-300971506.html.

4　Roger Connors and Tom Smith, *How Did That Happen? Holding People Accountable for Results the Positive, Principled Way* (New York, NY: Portfolio, 2011).

5　Henry Kimsey-House, Karen Kimsey-House, Phillip Sandahl, and Laura Whitworth, *Co-Active Coaching: The Proven Framework for Transformative Conversations at Work and in Life*, 4th ed. (Boston, MA: Nicholas Brealey Publishing, 2018).

6　Daniel Goleman, Richard E. Boyatzis, and Annie McKee, *Primal Leadership: Unleashing the Power of Emotional Intelligence* (Boston, MA: Harvard Business Review Press, 2013), 60.

Chapter 4: The Weight of Words

1   Chris McChesney, Sean Covey, and Jim Huling, *The 4 Disciplines of Execution: Achieving Your Wildly Important Goals* (New York: Free Press, 2016).

2   Talya Bauer and Berrin Erdogan, "Organizational Socialization: The Effective Onboarding of New Employees," in *Handbook of Industrial and Organizational Psychology*, vol. 3, *Maintaining, Expanding, and Contracting the Organization,* ed. S. Zedeck et al. (Washington, DC: American Psychological Association, 2011), 51–64.

3   Roy Maurer, "New Employee Onboarding Guide," Talent Acquisition, Society for Human Resource Management (SHRM), shrm.org/resourcesandtools/hr-topics/talent-acquisition/pages/new-employee-onboarding-guide.aspx.

4   See *Merriam-Webster*, s.v. "Orient," merriam-webster.com/dictionary/orient#h1.

5   See *Merriam-Webster*, s.v. "Retain," merriam-webster.com/dictionary/retain.

6   See Vocabulary.com, s.v. "Engage," vocabulary.com/dictionary/engage.

7   See *Cambridge English Dictionary*, s.v. "Empower," dictionary.cambridge.org/dictionary/english/empower.

Chapter 5: Systems for Communication and Connection

1   As cited in Robyn Hannah, "Dynamic Signal Study Finds U.S. Workforce Stressed and Ready to Quit," Dynamic Signal, March 20, 2019, dynamicsignal.com/2019/03/20/2019-employee-communication-and-engagement-study/.

2   Patrick Lencioni, *Death by Meeting: A Leadership Fable about Solving the Most Painful Problem in Business* (San Francisco, CA: Jossey-Bass, 2004).

3   Lencioni, *Death by Meeting*; Gino Wickman, *Traction: Get a Grip on Your Business* (Dallas, TX: BenBella, 2011); Jeffrey K. Liker, *The Toyota Way: 14 Management Principles from the World's Greatest Manufacturer*, 2nd ed. (New York: McGraw Hill Education, 2020).

Chapter 6: The SAY Leadership Factor

1   Julia Bonner, "3 Phrases Confident Leaders Use Every Day," *Inc.*, April 16, 2018, inc.com/the-muse/how-to-speak-sound-confident-leader-effective-communication.html.

2   Dr. Ron Bonnstetter and Bill J. Bonnstetter, "Words That Don't Work: A Pilot Study Examining Verbal Barriers," white paper, TTI Success Insights, 2016, images.ttisi.com/wp-content/uploads/2019/04/04145642/words_that_dont_work.pdf.

3   For physician-patient interactions, see Naykky Singh Ospina et al., "Eliciting the Patient's Agenda: Secondary Analysis of Recorded Clinical Encounters," *Journal of General Internal Medicine* 34 (2019): 36–40, doi.org/10.1007/s11606-018-4540-5; for male-female interactions, see, for example, Adrienne Hancock and Benjamin A. Rubin, "Influence of Communication Partner's Gender on Language," *Journal of Language and Social Psychology* 34, no. 1 (2014): 46–64, doi.org/10.1177/0261927X14533197.

4   Kimsey-House et al., *Co-Active Coaching*.

5   Michael Bungay Stanier, *The Coaching Habit: Say Less, Ask More & Change the Way You Lead Forever* (Vancouver: Page Two, 2016).

6   See Lou Solomon, "Two-Thirds of Managers Are Uncomfortable Communicating with Employees," *Forbes*, March 9, 2016, hbr.org/2016/03/two-thirds-of-managers-are-uncomfortable-communicating-with-employees.

7   Marshall Goldsmith, "10 Surefire Reasons to Try Feedforward!" LinkedIn, August 26, 2014, linkedin.com/pulse/20140826144932-2022319-10-surefire-reasons-to-try-feedforward/.

8   Christine Porath, "Give Your Team More-Effective Positive Feedback," *Harvard Business Review*, October 25, 2016, hbr.org/2016/10/give-your-team-more-effective-positive-feedback.

Chapter 7: Align and Inspire

1   Jenna Filipkowski, "Talent Pulse 3.2—Onboarding Outcomes: Fulfill
     New Hire Expectations," Research, Human Capital Institute (HCI),
     April 14, 2016, hci.org/research/talent-pulse-32-onboarding-
     outcomes-fulfill-new-hire-expectations.

2   As cited in Jeremy Auger, "Address New Hire Training Early to
     Speed Full Productivity," *TLNT*, October 16, 2018, tlnt.com/
     address-new-hire-gaps-early-to-speed-full-productivity/.

3   See Dictionary.com, s.v. "Preceptor," dictionary.com/browse/
     preceptor.

4   See Table 6 under January 2020 for healthcare support occupations
     in "Employee Tenure in 2020," US Department of Labor, Bureau of
     Labor Statistics, news release, September 22, 2020, bls.gov/news.
     release/pdf/tenure.pdf.

5   As cited in Madeline Laurano, "The True Cost of a Bad Hire,"
     research brief, Brandon Hall Group, August 2015, b2b-assets.
     glassdoor.com/the-true-cost-of-a-bad-hire.pdf.

Chapter 8: Engage and Empower

1   Ken Blanchard and Garry Ridge, *Helping People Win at Work: A
     Business Philosophy Called "Don't Mark My Paper, Help Me Get an A"*
     (Upper Saddle River, NJ: Pearson Education Group, 2009).

2   Connors and Smith, *How Did That Happen?*

3   As cited in Allana Akhtar, "Bosses, Take Note: Workers Say Lack of
     Engagement Is a Top Reason They'd Quit Their Jobs," *Business
     Insider*, June 12, 2019, businessinsider.com/the-main-reason-an-
     employee-would-quit-a-job-2019-6.

4   As cited in Tomas Chamorro-Premuzic, "Does Money Really Affect
     Motivation? A Review of the Research," *Harvard Business Review*,
     April 10, 2013, hbr.org/2013/04/does-money-really-affect-motiv.

5   Scott Judd, Eric O'Rourke, and Adam Grant, "Employee Surveys Are Still One of the Best Ways to Measure Engagement," *Harvard Business Review*, March 14, 2018, hbr.org/2018/03/employee-surveys-are-still-one-of-the-best-ways-to-measure-engagement.

6   This information was taken from Gallup's 2016 *State of the American Workplace* study, which is no longer available. You can access the information in Karlyn Borysenko, "How Much Are Your Disengaged Employees Costing You?" *Forbes*, May 2, 2019, forbes.com/sites/karlynborysenko/2019/05/02/how-much-are-your-disengaged-employees-costing-you/?sh=339f70434376.

7   You can find the 2017 Gallup *State of the American Workplace* report at gallup.com/workplace/238085/state-american-workplace-report-2017.aspx.

8   Harter and Mann, "The Right Culture."

9   Jonathon Thorp et al., "Workplace Engagement and Workers' Compensation Claims as Predictors for Patient Safety Culture," *Journal of Patient Safety* 8, no. 4 (December 2012): 194–201, doi.org/10.1097/PTS.0b013e3182699942.

10 Buhlman and Lee, "When Patient Experience and Employee Engagement Both Improve."

Chapter 9: Attract and Select

1   Sharon Soliday, "Entrepreneur Truth Telling in Telehealth," The Hello Foundation, March 2, 2020, thehellofoundation.com/schools/entrepreneur-truth-telling-in-telehealth/.

2   "Employee Tenure in 2020," US Department of Labor, Bureau of Labor Statistics.

3   "Healthcare Occupations," *Occupational Outlook Handbook*, Publications, US Bureau of Labor Statistics, bls.gov/ooh/healthcare/home.htm.

4   Raymond S. Nickerson, "Confirmation Bias: A Ubiquitous Phenomenon in Many Guises," *Review of General Psychology* 2, no. 2, (June 1998): 175–220, doi.org/10.1037/1089-2680.2.2.175.

5   You can visit the Equal Employment Opportunity Commission website at eeoc.gov.

6 "Avoiding Adverse Impact in Employment Practices," Resources and Tools, Society of Human Resource Management (SHRM), June 18, 2020, shrm.org/resourcesandtools/tools-and-samples/toolkits/pages/avoidingadverseimpact.aspx.

7 "Job Matching: The Key to Superior Performance," TTI Success Insights, blog, March 11, 2011, blog.ttisi.com/job-matching-key-superior-performance.

Chapter 10: The DO Leadership Factor

1 See Lexico.com, s.v. "Emotional Intelligence," lexico.com/definition/emotional_intelligence.

2 *Udemy In Depth: 2018 Employee Experience Report,* Udemy for Business, September 2018, research.udemy.com/wp-content/uploads/2018/09/FINAL-Udemy_2018_Employee_Experience_Report_20180918_B.pdf.

3 Daniel Goleman, *Emotional Intelligence: Why It Can Matter More Than EQ* (New York, NY: Bantam Books, 1995).

4 You can find additional, free resources, including links to my ebooks on EQ, on my website, thepeoplefirstbook.com/bonus.

Chapter 11: Plan, Execute, and Learn

1 Check out the LAMP Institute for Leadership program at aptahpa.org/page/LAMP.

2 There are hundreds of templates for the PDSA process online, but I've included links here to two of my favorites: IHI (Institute for Healthcare Improvement) uses a nonclinical approach to demonstrate the method: ihi.org/education/IHIOpenSchool/resources/Assets/PDSAworksheet_Instructions.pdf; this is a useful sample worksheet: fhop.ucsf.edu/sites/fhop.ucsf.edu/files/custom_download/QIToolkit_PDSAWorksheet.pdf.

3 Rafael Aguayo, *Dr. Deming: The American Who Taught the Japanese about Quality* (New York, NY: Touchstone, 1991).

Chapter 12: Change Is the Only Constant

1   Dori Meinert, "Executive Briefing: How to Combat Change Fatigue," *HR Magazine*, Society of Human Resource Management (SHRM), April 1, 2015, shrm.org/hr-today/news/hr-magazine/pages/0415-execbrief.aspx.

2   D. Ambrose, *Managing Complex Change* (Pittsburgh, PA: The Enterprise Ltd., 1987). This chart can also be found in a chapter titled "A Framework for Thinking about Systems Change," in *Restructuring for Caring and Effective Education: Piecing the Puzzle Together*, 2nd ed., ed. Richard A. Villa and Jacqueline S. Thousand (Baltimore, MD: P.H. Brooks, 2000), 97.

3   Chip Heath and Dan Heath, *Switch: How to Change Things When Change Is Hard* (New York: Broadway Books, 2010).

Chapter 13: The 7 Stages of Growth

1   James Fischer, *Navigating the Growth Curve: 9 Fundamentals That Build a Profit-Driven, People-Centered, Growth-Smart Company* (Growth Curve Press, 2006).

2   Taken from Goleman, Boyatzis, and McKee, *Primal Leadership*.

Chapter 14: The GROW Leadership Factor

1   For additional resources on productive conflict, visit thepeoplefirstbook.com.

2   "8 Keys to Succeeding as a Physician in Private Practice," Private Practices, AMA, February 17, 2020, am a-assn.org/practice-management/private-practices/8-keys-succeeding-physician-private-practice.

3   "DNA Profile," TTI Success Insights Australia, ttisuccessinsights.com.au/profiling-tools/dna-profile.

About the Author

AMY LAFKO, founder of Cairn Consulting Solutions, is a leadership and organizational design expert, mainstage speaker, author, and advisor. Formerly a leader in healthcare operations, she brings real-world lessons and inspirational ideas to a variety of industries to help organizations grow their people so they can grow their business. Visit thepeoplefirstbook.com for more information or to book Amy for your next event.

9 781774 581